Answer Book

Heinemann

Heinemann Educational Publishers
Halley Court, Jordan Hill, Oxford, OX2 8EJ
a division of Harcourt Education Ltd
www.heinemann.co.uk

Heinemann is a registered trademark of Harcourt Education Ltd

First published 2003

06 05 04 03
10, 9, 8, 7, 6, 5, 4, 3, 2, 1

ISBN 0 435 20727 X

Cover illustration by Dave Cockburn
Cover design by Paul Goodman
Designed by Tech-Set
Printed in Great Britain by Ashford Colour Press, Gosport, Hants

Contents

PUPIL BOOK

PB ■ 1

1 a 516
   b 4302
   c 80 907
      Each digit moves one place to the left.

2 a 250
   b 9090
   c 70 030
      Each digit moves two places to the left.
      A zero is written in the empty column as a 'place holder'.

3 a 47 kg, 470 kg
   b 309 kg, 3090 kg
   c 817 kg, 8170 kg
   d 2053 kg, 20 530 kg

4 a Sixty-nine thousand
   b Eight hundred and two thousand
   c Eight million five thousand

PB ■ 2

1 a 60
   b 450·9
   c 78·32
      Each digit moves one place to the right.

2 a 0·34
   b 8·7
   c 80·25
      Each digit moves two places to the right.
      Place holders may be required in the units column (or after the decimal point).

3 a £5692, £569·20, £56·92
   b £2781, £278·10, £27·81
   c £89 245, £8924·50, £892·45
   d £90 156, £9015·60, £901·56

4 a Nine
   b Five hundred and seventy
   c Ninety-eight

PB ■ 3

1 a 427 560 < 427 650
   b 712 099 < 712 100
   c 570 002 > 569 998
   d 818 053 > 817 503

2 a 15, 16, 17, 18, 19, 20
   b 453, 454, 455, 456, 457, 458, 459, 460
   c 15 480, 15 481, 15 482, 15 483, 15 484, 15 485, 15 486, 15 487, 15 488, 15 489, 15 490

3 a Sula scored more.
      Multiple answers are possible, from 35 782 to 35 870.
   b Brian scored more.
      Multiple answers are possible, from 612 000 to 612 808.
   c Sula scored more.
      Multiple answers are possible, from 700 457 to 700 464.
   d Brian scored more.
      Multiple answers are possible, from 912 000 to 912 999.

4 a Any numbers using all the digits and starting 45, 47, 48 or 49.
   b Answers depend on the 6-digit numbers made.

c The smallest 2 of the 12
   numbers.
d The largest 2 of the 12
   numbers.
e Answers depend on the numbers
   made in *a*.
   Smallest possible difference: 9
f The largest and the smallest of
   the 12 numbers.

(?) There are 24 numbers in total.

PB ■ 4

1 *a* =
   b >
   c >
   d >

2 *a* Multiple answers are possible,
      including:
      51 and 69, 51 and 70, 51 and
      71, 51 and 72, 52 and 73,
      510 and 530, 1365 and 1385,
      16 583 and 16 601...
   b Any combination of:
      one of numbers 100 to 104 with
      one of numbers 120 to 126, or
      one of numbers 105 to 111 with
      one of numbers 127 to 133, or
      one of numbers 112 to 118 with
      one of numbers 134 to 140, or
      one of numbers 119 to 125 with
      one of numbers 141 to 147, or
      one of numbers 126 to 132 with
      148 or 149
   c Multiple answers are possible,
      including any combination of: one
      of numbers 2001 to 2006 with
      one of numbers 2035 to 2043, or
      one of numbers 2007 to 2015
      with one of numbers 2044 to
      2052, or one of numbers 2016 to
      2024 with one of numbers 2053
      to 2061, ...

3 *a* One of: 4801, 4811, 4821,
      4831, 4841, 4851, 4861,
      4871, 4881 or 4891 with one of
      4069, 4169, 4269, 4369,
      4469, 4569, 4669 or 4769; or
      4871, 4881 or 4891 with 4869.
   b One of: 1002, 1102, 1202,
      1302 or 1402 with one of 1501,
      1511, 1521, 1531, 1541,
      1551, 1561, 1571, 1581 or
      1591; or 1502 with one of
      1511, 1521, 1531, ... 1591
   c One of: 72 676 to 72 679,
      82 670 to 82 679, 92 670 to
      92 679.

4 Any ten numbers between 240 001
   and 249 999.

5 Multiple answers are possible, e.g.
   $487 < 513$.

(?) The answers from question 5 can be
   reversed to form the answers to this
   question.

PB ■ 5

1 *a* 2400 (60×40),
      $63 \times 42 = 2646$
   b 10 000 (400×25),
      $395 \times 25 = 9875$
   c 450 ($150 + 300$),
      $166 + 293 = 459$
   d 300 ($700 - 400$),
      $681 - 379 = 302$
   e 70 ($560 \div 8$), $578 \div 8 = 72.25$
   f 100 ($500 \div 5$), $462 \div 5.5 = 84$

2 *a* 25·2 m
   b 22·4 m
   c 18·4 m
   d 10·92 m
   e 12·85 m
   f 22·32 m

3 Child's own answers.

PB ■ 6

1 a $^-27, ^-2, 0, 9, 16$
　b $^-14, ^-12, ^-1, 26, 34$
　c $^-39, ^-32, ^-3, 4, 17$
　d $^-75, ^-61, ^-19, ^-3, 59$

2 $6 + 6, 5 + 7, 4 + 8, 3 + 9, 2 + 10,$
　$1 + 11, 0 + 12, ^-1 + 13, ^-2 + 14,$
　$^-3 + 15, ^-4 + 16, ^-5 + 17,$
　$^-6 + 18, ^-7 + 19, ^-8 + 20 \ldots$

❓ $24 - 12, 25 - 13, 26 - 14,$
　$27 - 15, 28 - 16, 29 - 17,$
　$30 - 18, 31 - 19 \ldots$
　$6 - ^-6, 7 - ^-5, 8 - ^-4, 9 - ^-3,$
　$10 - ^-2, 11 - ^-1, 12 - 0 \ldots$

PB ■ 7

1 a $1 \times 1 = 1$
　　$2 \times 2 = 4$
　　$3 \times 3 = 9$
　　$4 \times 4 = 16$
　　$5 \times 5 = 25$
　　$6 \times 6 = 36$
　　$7 \times 7 = 49$
　　$8 \times 8 = 64$
　　$9 \times 9 = 81$
　　$10 \times 10 = 100$
　b $1 \times 1 \times 1 = 1$
　　$2 \times 2 \times 2 = 8$
　　$3 \times 3 \times 3 = 27$
　　$4 \times 4 \times 4 = 64$
　　$5 \times 5 \times 5 = 125$
　　$6 \times 6 \times 6 = 216$
　　$7 \times 7 \times 7 = 343$
　　$8 \times 8 \times 8 = 512$
　　$9 \times 9 \times 9 = 729$
　　$10 \times 10 \times 10 = 1000$
　c $1 \times 1 \times 1 \times 1 = 1$
　　$2 \times 2 \times 2 \times 2 = 16$
　　$3 \times 3 \times 3 \times 3 = 81$
　　$4 \times 4 \times 4 \times 4 = 256$
　　$5 \times 5 \times 5 \times 5 = 625$
　　$6 \times 6 \times 6 \times 6 = 1296$
　　$7 \times 7 \times 7 \times 7 = 2401$
　　$8 \times 8 \times 8 \times 8 = 4096$

$9 \times 9 \times 9 \times 9 = 6561$
$10 \times 10 \times 10 \times 10 = 10\,000$
Answers are alternately odd and even.

2 a $2^2 - 1^2 = 3$
　　$3^2 - 2^2 = 5$
　　$4^2 - 3^2 = 7$
　　$5^2 - 4^2 = 9$
　　$6^2 - 5^2 = 11$
　　$7^2 - 6^2 = 13$
　　$8^2 - 7^2 = 15$
　　$9^2 - 8^2 = 17$
　　$10^2 - 9^2 = 19$
　b $(2 \times 2 \times 2) - (1 \times 1 \times 1) = 7$
　　$(3 \times 3 \times 3) - (2 \times 2 \times 2) = 19$
　　$(4 \times 4 \times 4) - (3 \times 3 \times 3) = 37$
　　$(5 \times 5 \times 5) - (4 \times 4 \times 4) = 61$
　　$(6 \times 6 \times 6) - (5 \times 5 \times 5) = 91$
　　$(7 \times 7 \times 7) - (6 \times 6 \times 6) = 127$
　　$(8 \times 8 \times 8) - (7 \times 7 \times 7) = 169$
　　$(9 \times 9 \times 9) - (8 \times 8 \times 8) = 217$
　　$(10 \times 10 \times 10) - (9 \times 9 \times 9) = 271$
　c $(2 \times 2 \times 2 \times 2) - (1 \times 1 \times 1 \times 1)$
　　　$= 15$
　　$(3 \times 3 \times 3 \times 3) - (2 \times 2 \times 2 \times 2)$
　　　$= 65$
　　$(4 \times 4 \times 4 \times 4) - (3 \times 3 \times 3 \times 3)$
　　　$= 175$
　　$(5 \times 5 \times 5 \times 5) - (4 \times 4 \times 4 \times 4)$
　　　$= 369$
　　$(6 \times 6 \times 6 \times 6) - (5 \times 5 \times 5 \times 5)$
　　　$= 671$
　　$(7 \times 7 \times 7 \times 7) - (6 \times 6 \times 6 \times 6)$
　　　$= 1105$
　　$(8 \times 8 \times 8 \times 8) - (7 \times 7 \times 7 \times 7)$
　　　$= 1695$
　　$(9 \times 9 \times 9 \times 9) - (8 \times 8 \times 8 \times 8)$
　　　$= 2465$
　　$(10 \times 10 \times 10 \times 10) - (9 \times 9 \times 9 \times 9)$
　　　$= 3439$
　All answers are odd.

3 a $4, 6, 8, \ldots$
　b $0, 2, 4, \ldots$
　c $4, 8, 12, \ldots$

d There are always 4 more red pegs than blue pegs.
The red pegs plus the blue pegs equals the total number of pegs.

(?) The most likely sequences are:
Red: 3, 4, 5, ...
Blue: 0, 2, 4, ...
Total: 3, 6, 9, ...

PB ■ 8

1 a 31, 37, 43, 49, 55, 61, 67, 73, 79, 85, 91, 97, 103
b 41, 50, 59, 68, 77, 86, 95, 104
c 38, 46, 54, 62, 70, 78, 86, 94, 102

2 1, 3, 6, 10, 15, 21, 28, 36, 45, 55, 66, 78, 91, 105
1 and 36 are triangular square numbers.

3

Number of colours	2	3	4	5	6	7
Number of pairs	1	3	6	10	15	21

The answers are triangular numbers.

PB ■ 9

1 a 0·2, 0·4, 0·6, 0·8, 1·0, 1·2, 1·4, 1·6
b 0·5, 1, 1·5, 2, 2·5, 3, 3·5, 4

2 a 9·9, 9·8, 9·7, 9·6, 9·5, 9·4, 9·3, 9·2
b 9·75, 9·5, 9·25, 9·0, 8·75, 8·5, 8·25, 8·0

3 Child's own answers.

PB ■ 10

1 a 15, 30, 45, 60, 90
b 14, 28, 42, 56, 70
c 36, 72

2 a Two of: 300, 315, 330, 345, 360, 375, 390.
b Two of: 308, 322, 336, 350, 364, 378, 392.
c Two of: 324, 360, 396.

3 a False
b True
c True – a diagonal

4 The sums of each diagonal of a 2×2 square from the multiplication square are consecutive numbers.
For example $2 \times 5 + 3 \times 6$ and $3 \times 5 + 2 \times 6$
The first is 5 less and 6 more than the second, a difference of 1.

(?) The sums of each diagonal of a 3×3 square from the multiplication square differ by 4 and of a 4×4 square differ by 10.

PB ■ 11

1 124 is divisible by 2, 4
124 is not divisible by 3, 5, 6, (7), 8, 9, 10

2 a 936 is divisible by 2, 3, 4, 6, 8, 9
936 is not divisible by 5, (7), 10
b 531 is divisible by 3, 9
531 is not divisible by 2, 4, 5, 6, (7), 8, 10
c 284 is divisible by 2, 4
284 is not divisible by 3, 5, 6, (7), 8, 9, 10
d 115 is divisible by 5
115 is not divisible by 2, 3, 4, 6, (7), 8, 9, 10
e 1350 is divisible by 2, 3, 5, 6, 9, 10
1350 is not divisible by 4, (7), 8

3 Numbers that are divisible by 6 only (written in the left-hand circle):

1002, 1014, 1020, 1026, 1038, 1044, 1050, 1062, 1068, 1074, 1086, 1092, 1098, 1110, 1116, 1122, 1134, 1140, 1146, 1158, 1164, 1170, 1182, 1188, 1194.

Numbers that are divisible by 8 only (written in the right-hand circle):

1000, 1016, 1024, 1040, 1048, 1064, 1072, 1088, 1096, 1112, 1120, 1136, 1144, 1160, 1168, 1184, 1192.

Numbers that are divisible by both 6 and 8 (written in the intersection of the two circles):

1008, 1032, 1056, 1080, 1104, 1128, 1152, 1176, 1200.

All other numbers between 1000 and 1200 are divisible by neither 6 nor 8 and are written outside the circles.

? Numbers that are divisible by 6 only (written in the left-hand circle):

2004, 2010, 2022, 2028, 2034, 2046, 2052, 2058, 2070, 2076, 2082, 2094, 2100, 2106, 2118, 2124, 2130, 2142, 2148, 2154, 2166, 2172, 2178, 2190, 2196.

Numbers that are divisible by 8 only (written in the right-hand circle):

2000, 2008, 2024, 2032, 2048, 2056, 2072, 2080, 2096, 2104, 2120, 2128, 2144, 2152, 2168, 2176, 2192, 2200.

Numbers that are divisible by both 6 and 8 (written in the intersection of the two circles):

2016, 2040, 2064, 2088, 2112, 2136, 2160, 2184.

All other numbers are divisible by neither 6 nor 8 and are written outside the two circles.

PB ■ 12

1 **a** 6, 12, 18, 24, 30
   b 36, 42, 48, 54, 60
   c 6

2 **a** 12, 24, 36, 48, 60, 72, 84, 96, 108, 120
   b 24, 48, 72, 96, 120, 144, 168, 192, 216, 240
   c 15, 30, 45, 60, 75, 90, 105, 120, 135, 150
   d 14, 28, 42, 56, 70, 84, 98, 112, 126, 140

3 **a** 10
   b 21
   c 8
   d 18

4 **a** Possible answers: 20, 110 or 200.
   b Child's own answers.

PB ■ 13

1 **a** 49, 4900, 490 000, 49 000 000
   b 121, 12 100, 1 210 000, 121 000 000

2 $3 = 2^2 - 1^2$
   $5 = 3^2 - 2^2$
   $7 = 4^2 - 3^2$ $8 = 3^2 - 1^2$
   $9 = 5^2 - 4^2$
   $11 = 6^2 - 5^2$ $12 = 4^2 - 2^2$
   $13 = 7^2 - 6^2$
   $15 = 8^2 - 7^2$ $16 = 5^2 - 3^2$
   $17 = 9^2 - 8^2$
   $19 = 10^2 - 9^2$ $20 = 6^2 - 4^2$
   $21 = 11^2 - 10^2$
   $23 = 12^2 - 11^2$ $24 = 7^2 - 5^2$
   $25 = 13^2 - 12^2$
   $27 = 14^2 - 13^2$ $28 = 8^2 - 6^2$
   $29 = 15^2 - 14^2$
   $31 = 16^2 - 15^2$ $32 = 9^2 - 7^2$
   $33 = 17^2 - 16^2$
   $35 = 18^2 - 17^2$ $36 = 10^2 - 8^2$

$37 = 19^2 - 18^2$
$39 = 20^2 - 19^2$ $40 = 11^2 - 9^2$
$41 = 21^2 - 20^2$
$43 = 22^2 - 21^2$ $44 = 12^2 - 10^2$
$45 = 23^2 - 22^2$
$47 = 24^2 - 23^2$ $48 = 13^2 - 11^2$
$49 = 25^2 - 24^2$

? $5 = 1^2 + 2^2$
$10 = 1^2 + 3^2$
$13 = 2^2 + 3^2$
$17 = 4^2 + 1^2$
$20 = 4^2 + 2^2$
$25 = 4^2 + 3^2$
$26 = 5^2 + 1^2$
$29 = 5^2 + 2^2$
$34 = 5^2 + 3^2$
$37 = 6^2 + 1^2$
$40 = 6^2 + 2^2$
$45 = 6^2 + 3^2$
$50 = 7^2 + 1^2$

PB ■ 14

1 *a* 32
 b 32, 44, 36
 c 32, 44, 36
 d 36, 75
 e 36
 f 36
 g 75
 h 31

2 *a* 2, 3, 5, 7
    11, 13, 17, 19
    23, 29
    31, 37
    41, 43, 47
    53, 59
    61, 67
    71, 73, 79
    83, 89
    91, 97
 b In the first decade 4 numbers are prime,

In the second decade 4 numbers are prime,
In the third decade 2 numbers are prime,
In the fourth decade 2 numbers are prime,
In the fifth decade 3 numbers are prime,
In the sixth decade 2 numbers are prime,
In the seventh decade 2 numbers are prime,
In the eighth decade 3 numbers are prime,
In the ninth decade 2 numbers are prime,
In the tenth decade 2 numbers are prime,
All prime numbers apart from 2 are odd and there is a repeating pattern of final digits.

3   Beyond the number 3 and up to 100, in the 6-column grid, the prime numbers occur in two columns of odd numbers.

? Beyond the number 3, in the 7-column grid and the 9-column grid, the prime numbers occur in diagonal lines. In the 8-column grid the prime numbers occur in four columns of odd numbers.

PB ■ 15

1 *a* $3 \times 2 = 6$,
    $3 \times 3 \times 2 = 18$
    $3 \times 3 \times 3 = 27$
    $5 \times 3 \times 2 = 30$
    $5 \times 3 \times 3 = 45$
    $5 \times 3 \times 2 \times 2 = 60$
    $7 \times 7 \times 2 = 98$
 b 60 has the most prime factors.
 c 6 has the least prime factors.

2 Possible answers include 6, 10, 14, 15, 21, 22, …

3 Possible answers include:
3 prime factors: 8, 12, 30, 42 …
4 prime factors: 16, 24, 40, 225 …
5 prime factors: 32, 80, 180, 675 …
6 prime factors: 64, 96, 160, …

PB ■ 16

1 **a** 13
b 17
c 23
d 31
e 41
f 53
The answers are all prime numbers.

2 **a** 41
b 43
c 47
d 53
e 61
f 71
The answers are all prime numbers.

3 96 has 12 factors.
1, 2, 3, 4, 6, 8, 12, 16, 24, 32, 48, 96

(?) 2-digit numbers with the fewest factors are the prime numbers: 11, 13, 17, 19 etc.

PB ■ 17

1 **a** $\frac{23}{6} = 3\frac{5}{6}$
b $\frac{47}{3} = 15\frac{2}{3}$
c $\frac{33}{4} = 8\frac{1}{4}$
d $5\frac{4}{5} = \frac{29}{5}$
e $6\frac{3}{10} = \frac{63}{10}$

2 Possible answers include:
$3 + 7 = 10, \frac{10}{5} = 2$

$3 + 11 = 14, \frac{14}{7} = 2$
$3 + 19 = 22, \frac{22}{11} = 2$
$5 + 17 = 22, \frac{22}{11} = 2$
$2 + 19 = 21, \frac{21}{7} = 3$
$5 + 7 = 12, \frac{12}{3} = 4$
$3 + 17 = 20, \frac{20}{5} = 4$
$7 + 13 = 20, \frac{20}{5} = 4$
$11 + 17 = 28, \frac{28}{7} = 4$
$7 + 3 = 10, \frac{10}{2} = 5$
$5 + 13 = 18, \frac{18}{3} = 6$
$11 + 19 = 30, \frac{30}{5} = 6$
$5 + 19 = 24, \frac{24}{3} = 8$
$7 + 17 = 24, \frac{24}{3} = 8$
$11 + 13 = 24, \frac{24}{3} = 8$
$11 + 19 = 30, \frac{30}{3} = 10$
$13 + 17 = 30, \frac{30}{3} = 10$
$17 + 19 = 36, \frac{36}{3} = 12.$

(?) Possible answers include:
$3 + 13 + 17 = 33, \frac{33}{11} = 3$
$3 + 13 + 19 = 35, \frac{35}{5} = 7$
$7 + 13 + 19 = 39, \frac{39}{3} = 13.$

PB ■ 18

1 **a** $\frac{1}{8}$
b $\frac{1}{12}$
c $\frac{1}{16}$
d $\frac{1}{8}$
e $\frac{1}{10}$
f $\frac{1}{6}$

2 **a** $\frac{1}{5}$ is twice $\frac{1}{10}$, $\frac{1}{10}$ is half of $\frac{1}{5}$
b $\frac{1}{2}$ is four times $\frac{1}{8}$, $\frac{1}{8}$ is a quarter of $\frac{1}{2}$
c $\frac{1}{2}$ is three times $\frac{1}{6}$, $\frac{1}{6}$ is a third of $\frac{1}{2}$
d $\frac{3}{4}$ is twice $\frac{3}{8}$, $\frac{3}{8}$ is half of $\frac{3}{4}$
e $\frac{2}{3}$ is four times $\frac{1}{6}$, $\frac{1}{6}$ is a quarter of $\frac{2}{3}$

3 **a** $\frac{1}{6}$
b 4
c $\frac{3}{8}$

PB ■ 19

1 **a** $\frac{1}{2}$

   b $\frac{2}{5}$

   c $\frac{1}{3}$

   d $\frac{1}{4}$

   e $\frac{1}{10} = \frac{2}{20}$ or $\frac{4}{10} = \frac{2}{5}$

   f $\frac{4}{8} = \frac{1}{2}$

2 **a** $\frac{1}{2}$

   b $\frac{3}{4}$

   c $\frac{4}{5}$

   d $\frac{1}{2}$

   e $\frac{1}{3}$

   f $\frac{5}{8}$

   g $\frac{4}{5}$

   h $\frac{1}{4}$

3 $\frac{1}{2} = \frac{3}{6}$, $\frac{1}{2} = \frac{4}{8}$, $\frac{1}{2} = \frac{5}{10}$, $\frac{2}{4} = \frac{3}{6}$, $\frac{2}{4} = \frac{5}{10}$,
$\frac{3}{6} = \frac{4}{8}$, $\frac{3}{6} = \frac{5}{10}$, $\frac{4}{8} = \frac{5}{10}$, $\frac{1}{4} = \frac{2}{8}$, $\frac{3}{4} = \frac{6}{8}$
$\frac{1}{3} = \frac{2}{6}$, $\frac{2}{6} = \frac{3}{9}$, $\frac{2}{3} = \frac{4}{6}$, $\frac{2}{3} = \frac{6}{9}$, $\frac{1}{5} = \frac{2}{10}$,
$\frac{2}{5} = \frac{4}{10}$, $\frac{3}{5} = \frac{6}{10}$, $\frac{4}{5} = \frac{8}{10}$

? Using 6 different digits each time, any combination of 3 from:
$\frac{1}{2} = \frac{2}{4} = \frac{3}{6} = \frac{4}{8} = \frac{5}{10} = \frac{6}{12} = \frac{7}{14} = \frac{8}{16} = \frac{9}{18}$
$= \frac{10}{20}$
$\frac{1}{4} = \frac{2}{8} = \frac{3}{12} = \frac{4}{16} = \frac{5}{20}$
$\frac{1}{3} = \frac{2}{6} = \frac{3}{9} = \frac{4}{12} = \frac{5}{15} = \frac{6}{18}$
$\frac{1}{5} = \frac{2}{10} = \frac{3}{15} = \frac{4}{20}$
$\frac{1}{6} = \frac{2}{12} = \frac{3}{18}$
$\frac{2}{3} = \frac{4}{6} = \frac{6}{9} = \frac{8}{12} = \frac{10}{15} = \frac{12}{18}$
$\frac{2}{5} = \frac{4}{10} = \frac{6}{15} = \frac{8}{20}$
$\frac{3}{5} = \frac{6}{10} = \frac{9}{15} = \frac{12}{20}$
$\frac{4}{5} = \frac{8}{10} = \frac{12}{15} = \frac{16}{20}$
$\frac{5}{6} = \frac{10}{12} = \frac{15}{18}$
(NOT, for example, $\frac{1}{2} = \frac{2}{4} = \frac{4}{8}$ as this uses 2 and 4 twice each.)

PB ■ 20

1 $\frac{1}{4}$, $\frac{3}{10}$, $\frac{3}{8}$, $\frac{2}{5}$, $\frac{1}{2}$, $\frac{2}{3}$, $\frac{5}{6}$

2 **a** $\frac{2}{4}$ and $\frac{3}{4}$, ($\frac{3}{4}$ circled)

   b $\frac{6}{10}$ and $\frac{5}{10}$ ($\frac{6}{10}$ circled)

   c $\frac{5}{20}$ and $\frac{4}{20}$ ($\frac{5}{20}$ circled)

   d $\frac{8}{12}$ and $\frac{9}{12}$ ($\frac{9}{12}$ circled)

   e $\frac{6}{15}$ and $\frac{10}{15}$ ($\frac{10}{15}$ circled)

   f $\frac{3}{8}$ and $\frac{6}{8}$ ($\frac{6}{8}$ circled)

3 **a** $\frac{1}{6}$, $\frac{2}{6} = \frac{1}{3}$, $\frac{3}{6} = \frac{1}{2}$, $\frac{4}{6} = \frac{2}{3}$, $\frac{5}{6}$

   b 3

   c 2

4 **a** $\frac{1}{4}$, $\frac{2}{4}$, $\frac{3}{4}$
3 in the set
Reduced to: $\frac{1}{4}$, $\frac{1}{2}$, $\frac{3}{4}$
1 has a denominator not 4
2 have a denominator still 4
$\frac{1}{5}$, $\frac{2}{5}$, $\frac{3}{5}$, $\frac{4}{5}$
4 in the set
None can be reduced.
All have a denominator still 5
$\frac{1}{7}$, $\frac{2}{7}$, $\frac{3}{7}$, $\frac{4}{7}$, $\frac{5}{7}$, $\frac{6}{7}$
6 in the set
None can be reduced.
All have a denominator still 7
$\frac{1}{8}$, $\frac{2}{8}$, $\frac{3}{8}$, $\frac{4}{8}$, $\frac{5}{8}$, $\frac{6}{8}$, $\frac{7}{8}$
7 in the set
Reduced to: $\frac{1}{8}$, $\frac{1}{4}$, $\frac{3}{8}$, $\frac{1}{2}$, $\frac{5}{8}$, $\frac{3}{4}$, $\frac{7}{8}$
3 have a denominator not 8
4 have a denominator still 8
$\frac{1}{9}$, $\frac{2}{9}$, $\frac{3}{9}$, $\frac{4}{9}$, $\frac{5}{9}$, $\frac{6}{9}$, $\frac{7}{9}$, $\frac{8}{9}$
8 in the set
Reduced to: $\frac{1}{9}$, $\frac{2}{9}$, $\frac{1}{3}$, $\frac{4}{9}$, $\frac{5}{9}$, $\frac{2}{3}$, $\frac{7}{9}$, $\frac{8}{9}$
2 have a denominator not 9
6 have a denominator still 9
$\frac{1}{10}$, $\frac{2}{10}$, $\frac{3}{10}$, $\frac{4}{10}$, $\frac{5}{10}$, $\frac{6}{10}$, $\frac{7}{10}$, $\frac{8}{10}$, $\frac{9}{10}$
9 in the set
Reduced to: $\frac{1}{10}$, $\frac{1}{5}$, $\frac{3}{10}$, $\frac{2}{5}$, $\frac{1}{2}$, $\frac{3}{5}$, $\frac{7}{10}$, $\frac{4}{5}$, $\frac{9}{10}$
5 have a denominator not 10
4 have a denominator still 10

   b The sets that have no fractions that can be reduced have denominators that are prime numbers.

PB ■ 21

1 **a** $\frac{1}{5}$ of $45 = 45 \div 5 = 9$
   b $63 \div 8 = \frac{63}{8} = 7\frac{7}{8}$
   c $71 \div 10 = \frac{71}{10} = 7\frac{1}{10}$
   d $\frac{1}{100}$ of $500 = 500 \div 100 = 5$
   e $62 \div 5 = \frac{62}{5} = 12\frac{2}{5}$
   f $19 \div 8 = \frac{19}{8} = 2\frac{3}{8}$

2 **a** 18
   b 35
   c 45
   d 60
   e 60 litres
   f 24 m
   g 84 grams
   h 90 kg
   i 18 minutes

3 **a** $\frac{3}{10}$
   b 300 ml

4 **a** $\frac{1}{20}$
   b 14

5 **a** 3
   b $\frac{1}{4}$
   c 91
   d $\frac{91}{365}$

PB ■ 22

1 Pattern A: There are **2** blue tiles for every **1** white tile.
   Pattern B: There are **2** white tiles in every **3** tiles.
   Pattern C: There are **3** blue tiles in every **4** tiles.

2 B R R R B R R R B R R R

3 **a** B R R B R R B R R B R R
   2 in every 3 tiles are red.
   $\frac{2}{3}$ of the pattern is red.
   b B B B R B B B R B B B R
   3 in every 4 tiles are blue.
   $\frac{3}{4}$ of the pattern is blue.

4 24

5 **a** 3 in every 4 are shot-putters.
   $\frac{3}{4}$
   b 4

PB ■ 23

1 **a** three thousandths
   b two tenths
   c five hundredths
   d eight hundredths and five thousandths or eighty-five thousandths
   e three tenths and nine hundredths or thirty-nine hundredths
   f six and five tenths or sixty-five tenths
   g two tenths and one hundredth and four thousandths or two hundred and fourteen thousandths
   h seven and eight tenths and one hundredth and two thousandths or seven and eight hundred and twelve thousandths

2 **a** 0·406
   b 0·017
   c 0·159
   d 0·803
   e 14·037

3 **a** Thirty-six thousandths
   b Three and eight tenths four hundredths and four thousandths or three and eight hundred and forty-four thousandths
   c Nine tenths and three thousandths
   d One and five thousandths
   e Seventeen and one tenth and two thousandths or seventeen and one hundred and two thousandths

PB ■ 24

1 **a** 1·86, 1·88, 1·9, 1·92
   b 3·99, 4·01, 4·03, 4·05
   c 7, 6·98, 6·96, 6·94

d 2·61, 2·59, 2·57, 2·55
e 6·98, 7, 7·02, 7·04
f 5·71, 5·69, 5·67, 5·65

2 a 15·05, 5·62, 5·43, 5·34, 5·09
b 1·5, 1·425, 1·3, 1·285, 1·25

3 a 4·253, 4·325, 4·352, 4·523, 4·532
b 8·368, 8·386, 8·638, 8·836, 8·863

4 a Any number from 324·351 to 324·359 miles.
b Any number from 497·431 to 497·439 miles.
c Any number from 465·251 to 465·259 miles.
d Any number from 393·991 to 393·999 miles.

5 a 2·962 km, 2·438 km, 2·112 km
b Possible answers include any three times from 45·121 minutes to 47·379 minutes.

6 Gold 55·685 kg
Silver 55·645 kg
Bronze 54·885 kg

PB ■ 25

1 a Possible answers:
3·65, 3·66, 3·67, 3·68, 3·69.
b 9·42
c Possible answers:
4·61, 4·62, 4·63, 4·64.
d Possible answers:
2·35, 2·36, 2·37, 2·38, 2·39.
e Possible answers:
5·65, 5·66, 5·67, 5·68, 5·69, 5·70, 5·71, 5·72, 5·73, 5·74.
f 8·17
g Possible answers:
7·75, 7·76, 7·77, 7·78, 7·79, 7·80, 7·81, 7·82, 7·83, 7·84.

h Possible answers:
6·25, 6·26, 6·27, 6·28, 6·29.
i Possible answers:
1·85, 1·86, 1·87, 1·88, 1·89, 1.90, 1·91, 1·92, 1·93, 1·94.

2 a 35·4 kg
b 12·5 min
c 81·8 ml
d 10·5 sec
e 142·6 cm
f 109·3 m
g 151·8 km
h £135·90

3 a 1·55, 1·56, 1·57, 1·58, 1·59, 1.60, 1·61, 1·62, 1·63, 1·64
b 7·75, 7·76, 7·77, 7·78, 7·79, 7.80, 7·81, 7·82, 7·83, 7·84
c 4·15, 4·16, 4·17, 4·18, 4·19, 4.20, 4·21, 4·22, 4·23, 4·24
d 4·95, 4·96, 4·97, 4·98, 4·99, 5.00, 5·01, 5·02, 5·03, 5·04

4 a Any number from 5·50 to 6·49.
b Any number from 10·50 to 11·49.
c Any number from 0·50 to 1·49.
d Any number from 79·50 to 80·49.

5 9 ÷ 4 = 2·25, 7 ÷ 4 = 1·75,
6 ÷ 8 = 0·75, 5 ÷ 4 = 1·25,
3 ÷ 4 = 0·75, 1 ÷ 4 = 0·25
Rounded to one decimal place:
9 ÷ 4 = 2·3, 7 ÷ 4 = 1·8,
6 ÷ 8 = 0·8, 5 ÷ 4 = 1·3,
3 ÷ 4 = 0·8, 1 ÷ 4 = 0·3.
The digits in the tenths column are either 3 or 8.

? Odd 2-digit numbers divided by 4 and even 2-digit numbers divided by 8 give answers with exactly 2 decimal places.

PB ■ 26

1 a $0.5 = \frac{1}{2}$

b $0.75 = \frac{3}{4}$

c $0.03 = \frac{3}{100}$

d $\frac{1}{5} = 0.2$, $\frac{2}{5} = 0.4$, $\frac{3}{5} = 0.6$, $\frac{4}{5} = 0.8$

2 a $4\frac{7}{20}$

b $1\frac{1}{5}$

c $6\frac{1}{20}$

d $8\frac{1}{8}$

e $2\frac{1}{4}$

3 a&b

Discus:

red $22\frac{1}{200}$ Gold: blue

blue $24\frac{21}{200}$ Silver: yellow

green $22\frac{23}{200}$ Bronze: green

yellow $23\frac{39}{40}$

High jump:

red $1\frac{107}{200}$ Gold: yellow

blue $1\frac{121}{200}$ Silver: blue

green $1\frac{13}{200}$ Bronze: green

yellow $1\frac{191}{200}$

Long jump:

red $3\frac{23}{40}$ Gold: yellow

blue $3\frac{91}{200}$ Silver: red

green $3\frac{19}{40}$ Bronze: green

yellow $3\frac{151}{200}$

4 a 100 m:

red 10·032 s

blue 11·257 s

green 10·305 s

yellow 11·145 s

400 m hurdles:

red 45·261 s

blue 45·749 s

green 45·003 s

yellow 45·048 s

b 100 m:

Gold: red

Silver: green

Bronze: yellow

400 m hurdles:

Gold: green

Silver: yellow

Bronze: red

PB ■ 27

1 a 0·3, 30%

b 0·45, 45%

c 0·7, 70%

d 0·5, 50%

e 0·75, 75%

f 0·2, 20%

g 0·28, 28%

h 0·95, 95%

2 a $\frac{30}{100}$

b $\frac{7}{25}$, $\frac{30}{100}$, $\frac{45}{100}$

c 30%, 45%, 50%, 20%, 28%

d 70%

e $\frac{30}{100}$, $\frac{1}{5}$, $\frac{7}{25}$

f 20%, 28%, 30%

3 a School A because 40% finished while only 33% finished from School B.

b School E because 90% beat the time while only 75% from School C and 80% from School D beat the time.

c School C because 60% were successful while only 29·6% from School A and 54·5% from School D were successful.

PB ■ 28

1 a 59%

b 0·34

c 67%

d 0·75, $\frac{5}{8}$, 51%, 80%

PB ■ 29

1 a $\frac{1}{4}$
   b $\frac{3}{10}$
   c $\frac{3}{4}$
   d $\frac{2}{5}$
   e $\frac{1}{10}$
   f $\frac{3}{5}$
   g $\frac{4}{5}$
   h $\frac{1}{5}$

2 a 1·5 kg
   b 6 cm
   c £30
   d 6·5 m
   e £105
   f 350 g
   g 1·2 l
   h 126 g

3 a £360
   b £270
   c £384
   d Child's own problems and
      answers.

4 10% of £500 = £50,
   10% of £600 = £60,
   20% of £250 = £50,
   20% of £300 = £60,
   20% of £450 = £90,
   20% of £500 = £100,
   20% of £700 = £140,
   25% of £200 = £50,
   25% of £400 = £100,
   25% of £600 = £150,
   30% of £200 = £60,
   30% of £300 = £90,
   30% of £450 = £135,
   30% of £500 = £150,
   40% of £150 = £60,
   40% of £250 = £100,
   40% of £350 = £140,
   50% of £100 = £50,
   50% of £200 = £100,
   50% of £300 = £500,
   50% of £450 = £225,
   60% of £100 = £60,
   60% of £150 = £90,
   60% of £250 = £150,
   60% of £700 = £420,
   70% of £200 = £140,
   70% of £600 = £420,
   75% of £200 = £150,
   75% of £300 = £225,
   90% of £100 = £90,
   90% of £150 = £135,
   90% of £250 = £225

PB ■ 30

1 a 20 kg
   b £170
   c 7 m
   d 52 g
   e 13p
   f 89 ml
   g £100
   h 9 cm

PB ■ 31

1 a 6250
   b 7786
   c 4354
   d 6892
   e 3667
   f 3344

2 a subtract 3215, add 268, add
      5946, subtract 6012
   b add 4203, add 1062, subtract
      6069, add 3080

3 a Town: 4906 km
      City: 5530 km
      Rovers: 8434 km
      County: 6996 km
   b Rovers
   c County
   d City
   e Town

1 Child's mental strategies to make:
   a 600
   b 642
   c 768
   d 976
   e 1262
   f 2568
   g 3576
   h 3560
   i 7572
   j 7556
   k 574·9
   l 577·1
   m 579·9
   n 586·9
   o 588·1.

2 Child's own answers to show that the trail always ends at 2000.

3 Multiple answers are possible, from 1500 and 4485 onwards.

4 Multiple answers are possible:

triangle	square
46	38·1
46·1 to 46·9	38·2 to 39
47	39·1
47·1 to 47·9	39·2 to 40
48	40·1
48·1 to 48·9	40·2 to 41
49	41·1
49·1 to 49·9	41·2 to 42
50	42·1
50·1 to 50·9	42·2 to 43
51	43·1
51·1 to 51·9	43·2 to 44
52	44·1
52·1 to 52·9	44·2 to 45
53	45·1
53·1 to 53·9	45·2 to 46
54	46·1
54·1 to 54·9	46·2 to 47
55	47·1
55·1 to 55.9	47·2 to 48
56	48·1
56·1 to 56·9	48·2 to 49
57	49·1
57·1 to 57·9	49·2 to 50

PUPIL BOOK

To give a difference of 8·9 the answers from question 4 can be modified by subtracting 1 from each square number in the table.
46 − 38·1 = 7·9
46 − 37·1 = 8·9.

PB ■ 33

1

△	⚡	📡	🏈	🏏	⛰	🎾	⚽	🏇	🏂
2	5	4	6	7	3	9	1	10	8

2 a&b Possible solution:
A = 10, B = 20, C = 30,
D = 120, E = 140, F = 130
Many solutions are possible.
For all:
A + E = 150
C + D = 150
B + F = 150.

3 a $29 + 16$
b Any 3 from:
$29 + 13 + 3 = 45$
$29 + 12 + 4 = 45$
$20 + 13 + 12 = 45$
$18 + 14 + 13 = 45.$
c Any 4 from:
$20 + 18 + 4 + 3 = 45$
$20 + 14 + 8 + 3 = 45$
$20 + 13 + 8 + 4 = 45$
$18 + 16 + 8 + 3 = 45$
$16 + 14 + 12 + 3 = 45$
$16 + 13 + 12 + 4 = 45.$

4 $46 = 10 + 11 + 12 + 13$
$47 = 23 + 24$
$48 = 15 + 16 + 17$
$49 = 24 + 25$
$50 = 11 + 12 + 13 + 14$
$51 = 25 + 26 = 16 + 17 + 18$
$52 =$
$53 = 26 + 27$
$54 = 12 + 13 + 14 + 15$
     $= 17 + 18 + 19$
$55 = 27 + 28$

PB ■ 34

1 a&b $9800 - 4900 = 4900,$
$9800 - 6600 = 3200,$
$9800 - 5700 = 4100,$
$7500 - 3300 = 4200,$
$6700 - 3300 = 3400,$
$8800 - 5600 = 3200,$
$6600 - 2300 = 4300,$
$5700 - 2300 = 3400$

2 a $0\cdot2$ m
  b $0\cdot36$ m
  c $0\cdot22$ m
  d $0\cdot93$ m
  e $0\cdot64$ m

3 a&b $0\cdot6$ and $0\cdot78$, total $= 1\cdot38$,
difference $= 0\cdot18$
$0\cdot6$ and $0\cdot87$, total $= 1\cdot47$,
difference $= 0\cdot27$
$0\cdot7$ and $0\cdot68$, total $= 1\cdot38$,
difference $= 0\cdot02$
$0\cdot7$ and $0\cdot86$, total $= 1\cdot56$,
difference $= 0\cdot16$
$0\cdot8$ and $0\cdot67$, total $= 1\cdot47$,
difference $= 0\cdot13$
$0\cdot8$ and $0\cdot76$, total $= 1\cdot56$,
difference $= 0\cdot04$

4 $22 = 3 + 19 = 5 + 17$
$24 = 5 + 19 = 7 + 17 = 11 + 13,$
$26 = 3 + 23 = 13 + 13 = 7 + 19$
$28 = 5 + 23 = 11 + 17$
$30 = 7 + 23 = 11 + 19 = 13 + 17$
$32 = 3 + 29 = 19 + 13$
$34 = 3 + 31 = 5 + 29 = 11 + 23$
     $= 17 + 17$
$36 = 5 + 31 = 7 + 29 = 13 + 23$
     $= 17 + 19$
$38 = 31 + 7 = 19 + 19$
$40 = 37 + 3 = 29 + 11 = 23 + 17$
$42 = 37 + 5 = 31 + 11$
     $= 29 + 13 = 23 + 19$
$44 = 41 + 3 = 37 + 7 = 31 + 13$
$46 = 43 + 3 = 41 + 5$

$48 = 43 + 5 = 41 + 7$
$\quad = 37 + 11 = 31 + 17 = 29 + 19$
$50 = 47 + 3 = 43 + 7$
$\quad = 37 + 13 = 31 + 19$

(?) Using 2 prime numbers that are less than 50, the largest number that can be made is 94 (47 + 47). 92 cannot be made.

PB ■ 35

1 *a* 10 862
  b 12 222
  c 10 401
  d 12 218

2 Child's own answers to show that the sums of 4-digit numbers and their reversals are all divisible by 11.

(?) Child's own answers to show that the sum of 2-digit numbers and their reversals are all divisible by 11. The sum of 3-digit numbers and their reversals and 5-digit numbers and their reversals, however, are not divisible by 11.

PB ■ 36

1 *a* 12 321
  b 28 793
  c 37 546

2 *a* Car 3 has travelled furthest (21 850 m) after 5 minutes.
  b Car 3 (21 850 m)
      Car 4 (19 645 m)
      Car 1 (18 708 m)
      Car 2 (17 791 m)

3 *a* Tom: £7008, Anna: £12 234, Ted: £19 675, Helena: £18 113
  b Ted
  c £1562
  d £713
  e £2039

PB ■ 37

1 *a* 48·69
  b 15·74
  c 174·22
  d 24·27
  e 474·37
  f 32·45

2 There are 20 possible answers, including:
  $147 \cdot 0 + 56 \cdot 49 + 156 \cdot 94 = 360 \cdot 43$,
  $147 \cdot 0 + 56 \cdot 49 + 149 \cdot 77 = 353 \cdot 26$,
  $147 \cdot 0 + 56 \cdot 49 + 185 \cdot 87 = 389 \cdot 36$,
  $147 \cdot 0 + 56 \cdot 49 + 161 \cdot 44 = 364 \cdot 93$,
  $147 \cdot 0 + 156 \cdot 94 + 149 \cdot 77 = 453 \cdot 71$,
  $147 \cdot 0 + 156 \cdot 94 + 185 \cdot 87 = 489 \cdot 81$,
  $147 \cdot 0 + 156 \cdot 94 + 161 \cdot 44 = 465 \cdot 38$, $147 \cdot 0 + 149 \cdot 77 + 185 \cdot 87 = 482 \cdot 64$,
  $147 \cdot 0 + 149 \cdot 77 + 161 \cdot 44 = 458 \cdot 21$, $147 \cdot 0 + 185 \cdot 87 + 161 \cdot 44 = 494 \cdot 31$.

3 *a* 565·6 g
  b 224·43 g
  c 731·13 g
  d 457·5 g
  e 160·47 g
  f 56·37 g
  g 660·6 g

PB ■ 38

1 *a* 5267
  b 903
  c 6220
  d 3963
  e 2629
  f 2422

2 *a* add 33 962, subtract 33 282, add 40 084, subtract 39 033, add 49 539

b add 34 243, subtract 29 493,
add 76 992, subtract 79 110,
add 57 933

3 *a* 5556, 15 565, 25 655, 36 555,
55 555
Abigail used the digits in order
each time, starting again from 1
when she reached 9, to make her
5-digit and 4-digit numbers.
b 10 009, 10 090, 10 900, 19 000
c $67\,891 - 2345 = 65\,546$
$78\,912 - 3456 = 75\,456$
$89\,123 - 4567 = 84\,556$
$91\,234 - 5678 = 85\,556$
differences:
9991, 9910, 9100, 1000
d The differences are always made
up of digits 1, 9 and or 0.
The position of the various digits
changes by movement to the right.
There is a repeating pattern in the
differences; the differences
increase by 81, 810, 8100 and
9009 then reduce by 81, 810
and 8100 with a 9009 difference
back to the start.

PB ■ 39

1 *a* 114·18
b 512·79
c 135·21
d 59·22
e 358·92
f 335·12

2 *a* football by 14·51 cm
b volley ball by 12 cm
c hockey ball by 2·08 cm
d volley ball by 13·98 cm
e croquet ball by 4·06 cm

3 $9·8 - 5·67 = 4·13$
$9·8 - 5·76 = 4·04$
$9·8 - 6·57 = 3·23$
$9·8 - 6·75 = 3·05$
$9·8 - 7·56 = 2·24$
$9·8 - 7·65 = 2·15$
$4·13 + 2·15 = 6·28$
$4·04 + 2·24 = 6·28$
$3·23 + 3·05 = 6·28$

? $9·87 - 6·5 = 3·37$
$9·87 - 5·6 = 4·27$
$9·86 - 7·5 = 2·36$
$9·86 - 5·7 = 4·16$
$9·85 - 7·6 = 2·25$
$9·85 - 6·7 = 3·15$
$4·27 + 2·25 = 6·52$
$4·16 + 2·36 = 6·52$
$3·37 + 3·15 = 6·52$

PB ■ 40

1 Child's own answer to show the
difference between:
a their estimate and £73·85
b their estimate and £44·55
c their estimate and £61·85.

2 Child's own answers to show that
the trail always ends at 200.

3 $(24 + 37) \times (42 + 87) = 61 \times 129$
$= 7869$
$(24 + 42) \times (37 + 87) = 66 \times 124$
$= 8184$
$(24 + 87) \times (42 + 37) = 111 \times 79$
$= 8769$

? $(37 - 24) \times (87 - 42) = 13 \times 45$
$= 585$
$(42 - 24) \times (87 - 37) = 18 \times 50$
$= 900$
$(87 - 24) \times (42 - 37) = 63 \times 5$
$= 315$
$(24 - 37) \times (87 - 42) = ^-13 \times 45$
$= -585$
$(24 - 42) \times (87 - 37) = ^-18 \times 50$
$= -900$
$(24 - 87) \times (42 - 37) = ^-63 \times 5$
$= -315$

$(37 - 24) \times (42 - 87) = 13 \times {}^-45$
$= -585$
$(42 - 24) \times (37 - 87) = 18 \times {}^-50$
$= -900$
$(87 - 24) \times (37 - 42) = 63 \times {}^-5$
$= -315$
$(24 - 37) \times (42 - 87)$
$= {}^-13 \times {}^-45 = 585$
$(24 - 42) \times (37 - 87)$
$= {}^-18 \times {}^-50 = 900$
$(24 - 87) \times (37 - 42)$
$= {}^-63 \times {}^-5 = 315$

PB ■ 41

1 Child's own answers.

2 a $6 \times 80 \times £5 \cdot 50 = £2640$
  b $(6 \times 80) - 413 = 480 - 413$
    $= 67$

3 a $413 \times 2 = 826$
  b $826 + 413 = 1239$
  c $6856 - 1239 - 253 = 5364$

4 a $(6856 - 1239) \times £8$
    $= 5617 \times £8 = £44\,936$
  b $(826 \times £5) + £44\,936$
    $= £4130 + £44\,936 = £49\,066$

5 a £64 492
  b £9·41

PB ■ 42

1 a $(12 \times 3) \times 10 = 36 \times 10 = 360$
    $12 \times (3 \times 10) = 12 \times 30 = 360$
  b $(8 \times 15) \times 5 = 120 \times 5 = 600$
    $8 \times (15 \times 5) = 8 \times 75 = 600$
  c $(18 \times 4) \times 2.5 = 72 \times 2.5 = 180$
    $18 \times (4 \times 2.5) = 18 \times 10 = 180$
  d $(14 \times 9) \times 5 = 126 \times 5 = 630$
    $14 \times (9 \times 5) = 14 \times 45 = 630$
  e $(3 \cdot 5 \times 14) \times 2 = 49 \times 2 = 98$
    $3 \cdot 5 \times (14 \times 2) = 3 \cdot 5 \times 28 = 98$
  f $(15 \times 1 \cdot 2) \times 5 = 18 \times 5 = 90$
    $15 \times (1 \cdot 2 \times 5) = 15 \times 6 = 90$

2 $8 \times 9 = (4 + 5) \times 8 = 4 \times 9 \times 2$
    $= 9 \times 8 = 2 \times 2 \times 18 = 72$
    $72 \div 9 = 72 \div (4 + 5) = 8$
    $8 \times 28 = 8 \times 3 \cdot 5 \times 8 = 224$
    $224 \div (2 \times 4) = 224 \div 8 = 28$
    $7 \times 8 = 3 \cdot 5 \times 16 = 2 \times 3 \cdot 5 \times 8$
    $= 2 \times 4 \times 7 = 56$

3 Multiple answers are possible.

4

$5 \times 0 \cdot 64 = 3.2$	$0 \cdot 64 \times 5 = 3 \cdot 2$
$3 \cdot 2 \div 5 = 0 \cdot 64$	$3 \cdot 2 \div 0 \cdot 64 = 5$
$5 \times 8 = 40$	$8 \times 5 = 40$
$40 \div 5 = 8$	$40 \div 8 = 5$
$5 \times 1 \cdot 6 = 8$	$1 \cdot 6 \times 5 = 8$
$8 \div 5 = 1 \cdot 6$	$8 \div 1 \cdot 6 = 5$
$5 \times 0 \cdot 8 = 4$	$0 \cdot 8 \times 5 = 4$
$4 \div 5 = 0 \cdot 8$	$4 \div 0 \cdot 8 = 5$
$0 \cdot 64 \times 10 = 6 \cdot 4$	$10 \times 0 \cdot 64 = 6 \cdot 4$
$6 \cdot 4 \div 0 \cdot 64 = 10$	$6 \cdot 4 \div 10 = 0 \cdot 64$
$0 \cdot 4 \times 8 = 3 \cdot 2$	$8 \times 0 \cdot 4 = 3 \cdot 2$
$3 \cdot 2 \div 0 \cdot 4 = 8$	$3 \cdot 2 \div 8 = 0 \cdot 4$
$0 \cdot 4 \times 4 = 1 \cdot 6$	$4 \times 0 \cdot 4 = 1 \cdot 6$
$1 \cdot 6 \div 0 \cdot 4 = 4$	$1 \cdot 6 \div 4 = 0 \cdot 4$
$0 \cdot 4 \times 10 = 4$	$10 \times 0 \cdot 4 = 4$
$4 \div 0 \cdot 4 = 10$	$4 \div 10 = 0 \cdot 4$
$0 \cdot 4 \times 1 \cdot 6 = 0 \cdot 64$	$1 \cdot 6 \times 0 \cdot 4 = 0 \cdot 64$
$0 \cdot 64 \div 0 \cdot 4 = 1 \cdot 6$	$0 \cdot 64 \div 1 \cdot 6 = 0 \cdot 4$
$8 \times 6 \cdot 4 = 51 \cdot 2$	$6 \cdot 4 \times 8 = 51 \cdot 2$
$51 \cdot 2 \div 8 = 6 \cdot 4$	$51 \cdot 2 \div 6 \cdot 4 = 8$
$8 \times 0 \cdot 8 = 6 \cdot 4$	$0 \cdot 8 \times 8 = 6 \cdot 4$
$6 \cdot 4 \div 8 = 0 \cdot 8$	$6 \cdot 4 \div 0 \cdot 8 = 8$
$4 \times 10 = 40$	$10 \times 4 = 40$
$40 \div 4 = 10$	$40 \div 10 = 4$
$4 \times 1 \cdot 6 = 6 \cdot 4$	$1 \cdot 6 \times 4 = 6 \cdot 4$
$6 \cdot 4 \div 4 = 1 \cdot 6$	$6 \cdot 4 \div 1 \cdot 6 = 4$
$4 \times 0 \cdot 8 = 3 \cdot 2$	$0 \cdot 8 \times 4 = 3 \cdot 2$
$3 \cdot 2 \div 4 = 0 \cdot 8$	$3 \cdot 2 \div 0 \cdot 8 = 4$
$10 \times 0 \cdot 8 = 8$	$0 \cdot 8 \times 10 = 8$
$8 \div 10 = 0 \cdot 8$	$8 \div 0 \cdot 8 = 10$

PB ■ 43

1 a $(12 \times 3) - (4 \times 5) = 16$
  b $(12 \div 3) \times 45 = 180$

c $(1 \div 2) \times 34 + 5 = 22$
d $(123 - 4) \times 5 = 595$
e $12 + (3 \times 4) - 5 = 19$
f $123 - (4 \div 5) = 122 \cdot 2$

2 *a* $36 \div (4 + 5) = 4$
  b $5 \times (9 - 1) = 40$
  c $(8 - 5) \times 3 = 9$
  d $(5 + 3 + 2) \div 2 = 5$ or
    $5 \times (3 + 2) = 25$
  e $(12 - 6) \div 3 = 2$
  f $(6 \div 2) \times 9 = 27$

3 Multiple answers are possible.

? Multiple answers are possible.

PB ■ 44

1 *a* 1·7
  b 2·4
  c 5·6
  d 7·3
  e 3·3
  f 4·7
  g 12·3
  h 16·4

2 *a* 3·91, 3·92, 3·93, 3·94
  b 8·65, 8·66, 8·67, 8·68, 8·69
  c 2·06
  d 9·15, 9·16, 9·17, 9·18, 9·19,
    9·20, 9·21, 9·22, 9·23, 9·24
  e 5·55, 5·56, 5·57, 5·58, 5·59,
    5·60, 5·61, 5·62, 5·63, 5·64
  f 7·15, 7·16, 7·17, 7·18, 7·19,
    7·20, 7·21, 7·22, 7·23, 7·24

3 Child's own answers.
  If the 2-digit number is a multiple of
  the 1-digit number the answer will
  be a whole number.
  If not, the answer will be a decimal
  that stops when the 1-digit number
  is 2, 4, 5 or 8, and is often a
  decimal that repeats if it is 3, 6 or 9.

PB ■ 45

1 *a* £0·70
  b £1·30
  c £0·37
  d £0·53
  e £0·09
  f £1·23
  g £3·67
  h £5·01

2 *a* £1·75
  b £1·25
  c £1·50
  d £1·45
  e £1·35
  f £1·24
  Pack f gives the cheapest price for
  each tape.

3 *a* £38·40
  b £19·20
  c £9·60
  d £6·40

4 *a* £11·75
  b £5·25
  c £12·56
  d £6·25

PB ■ 46

1 5 shelves

2 4 tickets

3 44 pages

4 7 vouchers

5 19 frames

6 20 times

7 16 minibuses

8 22 lengths

9 18 times

10 7 trays

11 Child's own question that requires the answer to be rounded up.

12 Child's own question that requires the answer to be rounded down.

PB ■ 47

1 **a** 4·2
  b 7200
  c 0·9
  d 6·4
  e 2·8
  f 9·9

2 **a** $2 \times \mathbf{75} = 150$
  b half of $\mathbf{580} = 290$
  c double $\mathbf{9 \cdot 4} = 18 \cdot 8$
  d divide 1380 by $2 = \mathbf{690}$
  e multiply 0·54 by $2 = \mathbf{1 \cdot 08}$
  f $2 \times 980 = 1960$

3 **a** 1740
  b £8800

PB ■ 48

1 **a** $1 \times 9 = \mathbf{9}$
    $2 \times 9 = \mathbf{18}$
    $4 \times 9 = \mathbf{36}$
    $8 \times 9 = \mathbf{72}$
    $16 \times 9 = \mathbf{144}$
    $32 \times 9 = \mathbf{288}$
    $\mathbf{64 \times 9 = 576}$
    $\mathbf{128 \times 9 = 1152}$

  b $1 \times 24 = \mathbf{24}$
    $2 \times 24 = \mathbf{48}$
    $4 \times 24 = \mathbf{96}$
    $8 \times 24 = \mathbf{192}$
    $16 \times 24 = \mathbf{384}$
    $32 \times 24 = \mathbf{768}$
    $\mathbf{64 \times 24 = 1536}$
    $\mathbf{128 \times 24 = 3072}$

  c $1 \times 32 = \mathbf{32}$
    $2 \times 32 = \mathbf{64}$
    $4 \times 32 = \mathbf{128}$
    $8 \times 32 = \mathbf{256}$
    $16 \times 32 = \mathbf{512}$
    $32 \times 32 = \mathbf{1024}$
    $\mathbf{64 \times 32 = 2048}$
    $\mathbf{128 \times 32 = 4096}$

2 **a** $42 \times 20 = 84 \times 10 = 840$
  b $45 \times 14 = 90 \times 7 = 630$
  c $40 \times 18 = 80 \times 9 = 720$
  d $16 \times 33 = 8 \times 66 = 528$
  e $21 \times 20 = 42 \times 10 = 420$
  f $5 \times 86 = 10 \times 43 = 430$
  g $80 \times 25 = 40 \times 50 = 2000$
  h $8 \times 12 \cdot 5 = 4 \times 25 = 100$
  i $160 \times 25 = 80 \times 50 = 4000$
  j $12 \cdot 5 \times 16 = 25 \times 8 = 200$
  k $14 \times 150 = 7 \times 300 = 2100$
  l $18 \times 500 = 9 \times 1000 = 9000$

3 **a** $1 \times 17 = \mathbf{17}$
    $2 \times 17 = \mathbf{34}$
    $4 \times 17 = \mathbf{68}$
    $8 \times 17 = \mathbf{136}$
    $\mathbf{16 \times 17 = 272}$
    $\mathbf{32 \times 17 = 544}$
    $\mathbf{64 \times 17 = 1088}$
    $\mathbf{128 \times 17 = 2176}$
    $\mathbf{256 \times 17 = 4352}$

  b Multiple answers are possible, from:
    $13 \times 17 = (1 \times 17) + (4 \times 17)$
             $+ (8 \times 17)$
             $= 17 + 68 + 136$
             $= 221$
    to:
    $39 \times 17 = (32 \times 17) + (4 \times 17)$
             $+ (2 \times 17) + (1 \times 17)$
             $= 544 + 68 + 34 + 17$
             $= 663.$

(?) $1 \times 23 = 23$
    $2 \times 23 = 46$

$4 \times 23 = 92$
$8 \times 23 = 184$
$16 \times 23 = 368$
$32 \times 23 = 736$
$64 \times 23 = 1472$
$128 \times 23 = 2944$
$256 \times 23 = 5888$

All multiples of 23 can be found as sums of the multiples above. For example:

$13 \times 23 = (1 \times 23) + (4 \times 23)$
$\qquad + (8 \times 23)$
$\qquad = 23 + 92 + 184$
$\qquad = 299.$

PB ■ 49

1 a $32 \times 6 = (30 \times 6) + (2 \times 6)$
$\qquad = 180 + 12$
$\qquad = 192$

b $36 \times 5 = (30 \times 5) + (6 \times 5)$
$\qquad = 150 + 30$
$\qquad = 180$

c $38 \times 7 = (30 \times 7) + (8 \times 7)$
$\qquad = 210 + 56$
$\qquad = 266$

or

$38 \times 7 = (40 \times 7) - (2 \times 7)$
$\qquad = 280 - 14$
$\qquad = 266$

d $42 \times 8 = (40 \times 8) + (2 \times 8)$
$\qquad = 320 + 16$
$\qquad = 336$

e $39 \times 8 = (30 \times 8) + (9 \times 8)$
$\qquad = 240 + 72$
$\qquad = 312$

or

$39 \times 8 = (40 \times 8) - (1 \times 8)$
$\qquad = 320 - 8$
$\qquad = 312$

f $54 \times 6 = (50 \times 6) + (4 \times 6)$
$\qquad = 300 + 24$
$\qquad = 324$

g $6.7 \times 8 = (6 \times 8) + (0.7 \times 8)$
$\qquad = 48 + 5.6$
$\qquad = 53.6$

h $7.6 \times 9 = (7 \times 9) + (0.6 \times 9)$
$\qquad = 63 + 5.4$
$\qquad = 68.4$

i $8.7 \times 9 = (8 \times 9) + (0.7 \times 9)$
$\qquad = 72 + 6.3$
$\qquad = 78.3$

2 a £234
b £301
c £522
d £370
e £522
f £784

PB ■ 50

1 a $4.25 \times 10 = \mathbf{42.5}$
b $3.8 \times 100 = \mathbf{380}$
c $0.42 \times \mathbf{100} = 42$
d $\mathbf{70} \div 100 = 0.7$
e $54 \div \mathbf{100} = 0.54$
f $\mathbf{0.9} \times 2 = 1.8$
g $\mathbf{1.5} \div 2 = 0.75$
h $0.5 \times 8 = \mathbf{4}$
i $49 \times 6 = \mathbf{294}$

2 a $80 \times 3 = 240$, $240 \div 3 = 80$,
$\qquad 3 \times 80 = 240$, $240 \div 80 = 3$
b $12.5 \times 8 = 100$,
$\qquad 100 \div 8 = 12.5$,
$\qquad 8 \times 12.5 = 100$, $100 \div 12.5 = 8$
c $3 \div 4 = 0.75$, $0.75 \times 4 = 3$
$\qquad 3 \div 0.75 = 4$, $4 \times 0.75 = 3$

3 a 9.3 cm
b 74 mm
c 1640 cm
d 21.17 m
e 1.04 m
f 0.55 m

4 Multiple answers are possible.

? Whichever digit, e.g. 2, is used,
$D = 2 - 2$
$1 = 2 \div 2$
and all numbers can be made.

PB ■ 51

1 a $9 \times 2 = \mathbf{18}$
$9 \times 20 = \mathbf{180}$
$90 \times 2 = \mathbf{180}$
$90 \times 20 = \mathbf{1800}$

b $7 \times 8 = \mathbf{56}$
$7 \times 80 = \mathbf{560}$
$70 \times 8 = \mathbf{560}$
$70 \times 80 = \mathbf{5600}$

c $8 \times 9 = \mathbf{72}$
$8 \times 90 = \mathbf{720}$
$80 \times 9 = \mathbf{720}$
$80 \times 90 = \mathbf{7200}$

2 a 1448 (approximately
$350 \times 4 = 1400$)

b 3042 (approximately
$500 \times 6 = 3000$)

c 3160 (approximately
$400 \times 8 = 3200$)

d 13 215 (approximately
$2500 \times 5 = 12\,500$)

e 19 008 (approximately
$3000 \times 6 = 18\,000$)

f 31 542 (approximately
$4500 \times 7 = 31\,500$)

3 Multiple answers are possible,
including:
$60\,060 \times 1$, 6006×10,
$30\,030 \times 2$, 3003×20,
$20\,020 \times 3$, 2002×30,
$15\,015 \times 4$, $12\,012 \times 5$,
$10\,010 \times 6$, 1001×60,
8580×7, 858×70,
5460×11, 546×110,
5005×12,
4620×13, 462×130,
4290×14, 429×140,
4004×15, 2860×21,
2730×22, 2310×26.

? Multiple answers are possible based
on the answers to question 3 with
one of each pair of numbers
factorised, e.g. $6006 \times 5 \times 2$.

PB ■ 52

1 a £100
b £10
c £10 000
d £100 000
e £2
f 4·17 euros
g £200
h 417 euros

PB ■ 53

1 a 540
b 612
c 1092
d 1302
e 1575
f 1786

2 a 5280 m²
b 6132 m²
c 7344 m²
d 13 320 m²

3 $476 \times 35 = 16\,660$
Child's own calculations using digits
3, 4, 5, 6, 7
Largest possible answer:
$743 \times 65 = 48\,295$
Smallest possible answer:
$467 \times 35 = 16\,345$
$645 \times 73 = 47\,085$.

? A 2-digit times a 3-digit
multiplication will give the same
answer as a 3-digit times 2-digit
multiplication for the same numbers.

PB ■ 54

1 a $42\frac{1}{4}$
b $71\frac{3}{4}$
c $69\frac{1}{5}$
d $76\frac{4}{5}$
e $118\frac{3}{5}$

f $159\frac{1}{4}$

g $82\frac{3}{8}$

h $89\frac{7}{8}$

2 a $26\frac{4}{5}$ l or 26·8 l

b £70·25

c $67\frac{3}{8}$ g or 67·375 g

PB ■ 55

1 a $68 \div \mathbf{4} = 17$

b $76 \div \mathbf{9 \cdot 5} = 8$

c $82 \div \mathbf{20 \cdot 5} = 4$

d $75 \div 6 = \mathbf{12 \cdot 5}$

e $86 \div 8 = \mathbf{10 \cdot 75}$

f $98 \div 8 = \mathbf{12 \cdot 25}$

2 a $377 \div 13 = \mathbf{29}$

b $416 \div 6 = \mathbf{69 \cdot 3}$

c $448 \div 32 = \mathbf{14}$

d $527 \div \mathbf{31} = 17$

e $406 \div \mathbf{29} = 14$

f $612 \div \mathbf{34} = 18$

g $\mathbf{378} \div 21 = 18$

h $\mathbf{238} \div 14 = 17$

i $\mathbf{782} \div 23 = 34$

PB ■ 56

1 a 12 and 4

b 27 and 3

2 12·5 l

3 19·5 l

4 10·4

5 8·2 m

6 74

7 12·3 kg

8 13·8 days – the stocks run out on the 14th day

9 9·2

10 9

PB ■ 57

1 a Divisible by 5: 405, 4120, 2835, 8640

b Divisible by 8: 88, 1224, 4120, 5672, 8640

c Divisible by 9: 117, 405, 1224, 2835, 3681, 8640

PB ■ 58

1 a 7·216 km

b 7·012 km

c 7·602 km

d 7·61 km

e 7·006 km

2 a 3457 m

b 2800 m

c 3390 m

d 4080 m

e 5605 m

f 970 m

3 a width = 35 m, perimeter = 210 m

b width = 24 m, perimeter = 144 m

c width = 13·5 m, perimeter = 81 m

d width = 17·5 m, perimeter = 105 m

4 a 0·1 m

b 1 m

c 1 m²

d $\frac{1}{10}, \frac{1}{1000}$

PB ■ 59

1 bronze: 40 mm, 4 cm

silver: 44 mm, 4·4 cm

gold: 48 mm, 4·8 cm

2 **a** 4·8 m
  b 44 m
  c 400 m

3 25 000

4 **a** 100
  b 375 m, 1500 m

5 **a** 0·4 m
  b 250

PB ■ 60
1 **a** 3·605 kg
  b 3·09 kg
  c 2·84 kg
  d 3·45 kg
  e 4·54 kg
  f 4·125 kg

2 **a** 7·2 kg
  b 6·2 kg
  c 5·7 kg
  d 6·9 kg
  e 9·1 kg
  f 8·3 kg

3 **a** 13 100 g, 15 900 g, 20 800 g, 23 700 g, 29 200 g, 35 600 g, 47 500 g, 57 300 g, 64 400 g
  b Between 2 and 4 years; 2800 g
  c Between 12 and 14 years; 11 900 g

4 Nina = 34 kg, Mary = 33·4 kg, Lisa = 32·6 kg

PB ■ 61
1 **a** 4·5 lb ≈ 2 kg
  b 6·75 lb ≈ 3 kg
  c 9 lb ≈ 4 kg

2 **a** 0·5 lb ≈ 230 g
  b 1·75 lb ≈ 790 g

  c 100 g ≈ 0·25 lb
  d 350 g ≈ 0·75 lb

3 **a** 910 g
  b 570 g
  c 340 g

4 **a** 2 eggs ≈ $\frac{1}{4}$ lb
  b 8 sausages ≈ 1 lb

5 10 eggs ≈ 600 g ≈ $1\frac{1}{4}$ lb
  12 sausages ≈ 681 g ≈ $1\frac{1}{2}$ lb

PB ■ 62
1 elephant = 4·1 tonnes
  polar bear = 0·68 tonnes
  tiger = 0·227 tonnes

2 **a** 10%
  b 25 lb or 11·3 kg per day

3 About 5 days

4 **a** 100%
  b 10%

5 $80 \times 0·112\,g = 8·96\,g$, 9 g to nearest g

PB ■ 63
1 **a** 700 ml
  b 300 ml
  c 50 ml

2 **a** 25 cl, 0·25 l
  b 75 cl, 0·75 l
  c 33 cl, 0·33 l
  d 150 cl, 1·5 l
  e 50 cl, 0·5 l
  f 87 cl, 0·87 l

3 **a** 3 for the price of 2: 2·7 l
    50% extra free: 2·25 l
  b 2·49 l

PB ■ 64

1 a 1·2 litres
  b 2·9 litres
  c 4·6 litres or 4·7 litres
  d 0·3 litres
  e 6·1 litres
  f 7·9 litres

2 a 7 pints
  b 12 pints
  c 15·5 pints
  d 3 pints
  e 7·25 pints

3 a 50%
  b 25%
  c 75%
  d 10%
  e 20%
  f 5%

4 a approximately 10 gallons
  b approximately 80 pints

PB ■ 65

1 Monday: 40 litres
  Tuesday: 34 litres
  Wednesday: 27 litres
  Thursday: 19 litres
  Friday: 11 litres

2 6 litres

3 Wednesday and Thursday

4 a 2 litres
  b 31 litres

5 a 45 litres
  b 10 gallons
  c 80 pints

PB ■ 66

1 a Perimeter A = 28 units
    Perimeter B = 26 units
    Perimeter C = 22 units
    Perimeter D = 28 units
  b A and D, B, C

2 a 8 cm
  b 14 cm
  c 14 cm
  d 18 cm

3 a

Perimeter of triangle in cm	Length of base in cm
10	2
20	4
30	6
40	8
50	10
60	12
70	14

  b $L = P \div 5$ or $P = 5L$
  c $L = 20$ cm

PB ■ 67

1 a 180 cm^2
  b 240 cm^2
  c 900 cm^2
  d 500 cm^2

2 100 of tile A
  75 of tile B
  20 of tile C
  36 of tile D

3 a $(10 \times 12) + (7 \times 3) = 120 + 21$
    $= 141$ cm^2, or
    $(10 \times 15) - (3 \times 3) = 150 - 9$
    $= 141$ cm^2
  b $(20 \times 10) + (8 \times 4)$
    $= 200 + 32 = 232$ cm^2, or
    $(10 \times 24) - (2 \times 4) = 240 - 8$
    $= 232$ cm^2

c $(30 \times 20) + (10 \times 15)$
$= 600 + 150 = 750\,\text{cm}^2$, or
$(30 \times 30) - (15 \times 10)$
$= 900 - 150 = 750\,\text{cm}^2$

d $(20 \times 5) + (20 \times 12)$
$= 100 + 240 = 340\,\text{cm}^2$, or
$(20 \times 25) - (20 \times 8)$
$= 500 - 160 = 340\,\text{cm}^2$

e $(9 \times 5) + (5 \times 4) = 45 + 20$
$= 65\,\text{cm}^2$, or $(9 \times 9) - (4 \times 4)$
$= 81 - 16 = 65\,\text{cm}^2$

f $(20 \times 10) + (30 \times 10)$
$+ (20 \times 10) = 200 + 300$
$+ 200 = 700\,\text{cm}^2$, or (30×30)
$- (10 \times 10) - (10 \times 10)$
$= 900 - 100 - 100 = 700\,\text{cm}^2$

PB ■ 68

1 a 9 m
b 6 cm
c 15 cm
d 30 mm

2 a 15 m
b 12 m
c 4 m

3 a $(12 \times 16) + (12 \times 20)$
$= 192 + 240 = 432\,\text{cm}^2$,
$(8 \times 12) + (28 \times 12)$
$= 96 + 336 = 432\,\text{cm}^2$,
$(28 \times 20) - (8 \times 16)$
$= 560 - 128 = 432\,\text{cm}^2$,

b The answers are all the same because the same area is being measured each time.

4 6 m by 6 m gives area of 36 m^2

(?) a 7 m by 8 m gives area of 56 m^2 but 7·5 m by 7·5 m gives 56·25 m^2

b 4 m by 5 m gives area of 20 m^2 but 4·5 m by 4·5 m gives 20·25 m^2

PB ■ 69

1 a 13:00
b 20:00
c 06:00
d 00:00
e 14:00
f 22:00

2 a Athens, Johannesburg
b Mexico City, Chicago
c Tokyo
d Vancouver

3 a 22:30
b 23:30
c 08:30
d 11:30

4 a 12:15
b 10:15
c 11:15
d 09:15

5 10 hr and 20 min

6 07:15

PB ■ 70

1 a 9 hr
b 3 hr 15 min
c 7 hr 15 min
d 3 hr 30 min

2 a sleeping
b sailing
c adventure course
d 5-a-side football

3 a 16:15 to 17:30
b 21:00 to 23:00
c 11:30 to 12:45 or 16:15 to 17:30
d 11:30 to 12:45
e 11:30 to 12:45 or 16:15 to 17:30

4 a 15 min
  b 1 hr 30 min
  c 1 hr 45 min
  d 1 hr 45 min

3 tetrahedron, cube (hexahedron), octahedron, dodecahedron and icosahedron (20 faces).

PB ■ 71

1

	No right-angled faces	1 right-angled face	More than 1 right-angled face
3 edges at each vertex	d, j		a, c, e, f, h
More than 3 edges at 1 or more vertices	g, i	b	

2 a

3-D shape	Number of			
	horizontal		vertical	
	faces	edges	faces	edges
cuboid	2	8	4	4
triangular prism	2	6	3	3

  b PQ is **parallel** to RS
    SP is **perpendicular** to SR
    YZ is **perpendicular** to WZ
    XY is **parallel** to WZ.

PB ■ 72

1 a Child's shape sequence labelled rectangle and parallelograms, 2 lines of symmetry drawn on the rectangle.

  b Child's shape sequence labelled rhombus and square, 2 lines of symmetry drawn on the rhombuses, 4 on the square.

c

Property of quadrilateral	square	rectangle	rhombus	parallelogram
all sides equal	✓		✓	
opposite sides equal		✓		✓
opposite sides parallel	✓	✓	✓	✓
all angles right angles	✓	✓		
opposite angles equal	✓	✓	✓	✓
no lines of symmetry				✓
fewer than 4 lines of symmetry		✓	✓	✓
4 axes of symmetry	✓			

2 A parallelogram has its opposite
sides **equal** and **parallel**.
A **rhombus** is a parallelogram with 4
equal sides and 2 lines of symmetry.

PB ■ 73

1 Child's pieces fitted to form square.

2 a

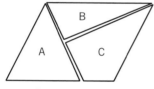

Parallelogram

b Drawn and labelled polygons.

Right angled triangle

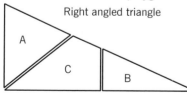

3 a Q, R and T make a square.
b Q, R and T make a rectangle,
  Q, R and T make a parallelogram,
  Q, R and T make a trapezium,
  Q, R and T make a right-angled
  isosceles triangle,
  T, S and Q make a rectangle,
  T, S and Q make a parallelogram,
  T, S and Q make a trapezium,

T, S and Q make a right-angled
isosceles triangle,
T, P and Q make a rectangle,
T, P and Q make a parallelogram,
T, P and Q make a trapezium,
T, P and Q make a right-angled
isosceles triangle.

PB ■ 74

1

Hexomino	Net of a cube	
	Yes	No
a	✓	
b		✓
c	✓	
d	✓	
e		✓
f	✓	
g	✓	
h		✓
i	✓	
j	✓	
k	✓	
l		✓
m	✓	
n	✓	
o	✓	

2 a

		6	2
4	5	3	
	1		

b

1	3		
	2	6	
		4	5

c

	3		
1	5	6	2
	4		

PB ■ 75

1 a 6
b 5
c 17

2 a 6
b 5
c 7

3 c

Skeletal cube	Number of cubes
3 × 3 × 3	20
4 × 4 × 4	32
5 × 5 × 5	44
6 × 6 × 6	56

d The number of cubes used increases by 12 cubes each time, as the skeletal cube grows bigger.
e A 7 × 7 × 7 skeletal cube would require 68 cubes.

PB ■ 76

1 a&b

Number of equal sides	Number of lines of symmetry
3	3
4	4
5	5
6	6
7	7
8	8
10	10
12	12
20	20

2 a $L = S$ or $S = L$
b Child's check that the formula works for heptagons and decagons.

3

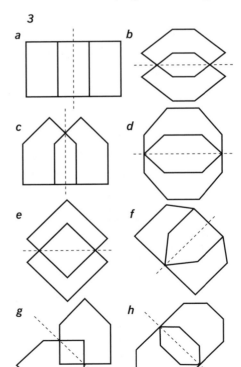

PB ■ 77

1 a (0, 2), (⁻5, 4), (⁻3, 1)
  b (0, 4), (⁻4, 4), (⁻4, 1), (⁻2, 1)
  c (0, 3), (⁻2, 4), (⁻4, 2), (⁻2, 1)

2

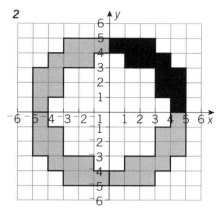

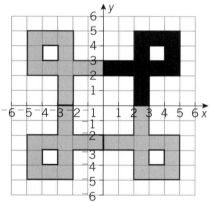

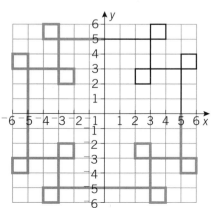

3 a&b

1st quadrant	$P_1 = (3, 5)$ $Q_1 = (2, 2)$ $R_1 = (6, 3)$
2nd quadrant	$P_2 = (⁻3, 5)$ $Q_2 = (⁻2, 2)$ $R_2 = (⁻6, 3)$
3rd quadrant	$P_3 = (⁻3, ⁻5)$ $Q_3 = (⁻2, ⁻2)$ $R_3 = (⁻6, ⁻3)$
4th quadrant	$P_4 = (3, ⁻5)$ $Q_4 = (2, ⁻2)$ $R_4 = (6, ⁻3)$

PB ■ 78

1 a A = (⁻6, 7)
    B = (⁻2, 8)
    C = (4, 7)
    D = (3, 4)
    E = (5, 2)
    F = (⁻3, 1)
    G = (⁻4, 3)
    H = (⁻1, 5)
    I = (6, 6)

  b Child's own coordinates of bowler and umpire.

2 a Peter's team

Coordinates of shot	Result
(⁻4, 5)	goal
(2, 3)	saved
(5, 6)	goal
(1, 3)	saved
(5, 1)	goal
(⁻3, 4)	goal
(⁻2,3)	goal

Linda's team

Coordinates of shot	Result
(1, 4)	saved
(⁻3, 3)	goal
(6, 5)	goal
(⁻2, 1)	goal
(0, 3)	saved
(⁻6, 3)	goal
(⁻1,3)	saved

  b Peter's team won.
  c 5 goals to 4.

PB ■ 79

1 Jason: tree swing
   Paul: trampoline
   Theo: climbing net
   Claire: rings
   Jan: tyres

2 *a* (⁻5, ⁻2)
  b (3, 3)
  c (⁻5, 3)
  d (6, ⁻2)
  e (4, 0)

3 *a* (⁻6, 1)
  b (⁻2, ⁻4)
  c (3, 3)

4 *a* rings
  b (2, ⁻3)
  c She walks 5 units to the right and 5 units up.

PB ■ 80

1 *a* 68°
  b 50°
  c 32°
  d 85°
  e 110°
  f 145°

2 *a* 115°
  b 65°
  c 115°
  d 35°
  e 145°
  f 35°
  g 125°
  h 55°
  i 125°
  j 50°
  k 130°
  l 50°
  m 108°
  n 72°
  o 108°
  p 76°
  q 104°
  r 76°

3 Child's own answers to show that the jet skier can cross the parallel courses of the power boats at any angle but the angles are the same for each power boat course.

PB ■ 81

1 *a&b*
  Child's own answers, measuring acute angles of scalene triangles.
  c 90° (or very close)

2 *a* 150°
  b 143°
  c 49°
  d 42°

3 Child's own work to show angles on a straight line always total 180°.

4 *a* A = 90°, 90°, 128°, 52°
     B = 70°, 70°, 110°, 110°
     C = 90°, 90°, 142°, 38°
  b The angle total for each trapezium should be 360°. Allow answers within 3°.
  c Child's own answers.

PB ■ 82

1 a equally likely
b not equally likely
c not equally likely
d equally likely
e equally likely
f equally likely

2 Child's own answers to show that the greater the sample size the smaller the difference between theoretical probability and experimental probability.

PB ■ 83

1 Statements marked on the probability scale at the following positions:
impossible: '0'
$\frac{1}{6}$ of distance: '6'
$\frac{1}{3}$ of distance: 'a multiple of 3'
                '2 or 3'
                'less than 3'
even chance: 'an even number'
                'an odd number'
                'has a factor of 2'
                'more than 3'
$\frac{2}{3}$ of distance: 'from 2 to 5'
$\frac{5}{6}$ of distance: 'less than 6'
certain: 'less than 7'
                'more than 0'.

2 Child's own answers examining the relationship between theoretical and experimental probability.

? Finding the totals of 2 dice gives 11 possible outcomes:
2: 1 in 36 chance
3: 1 in 18 chance
4: 1 in 12 chance
5: 1 in 9 chance
6: 5 in 36 chance
7: 1 in 6 chance
8: 5 in 36 chance
9: 1 in 9 chance

10: 1 in 12 chance
11: 1 in 18 chance
12: 1 in 36 chance

PB ■ 84

1

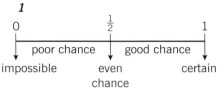

2 a Outcomes recorded on probability scale:
card from a black suit: $\frac{1}{2}$ or even chance
diamond: $\frac{1}{4}$ or poor chance
odd number: $\frac{1}{2}$ or even chance.
b–e Child's own record of experimental outcomes.

? Outcomes recorded on probability scale:
card from a red suit: $\frac{1}{2}$ or even chance
a spade: $\frac{1}{4}$
even number: $\frac{1}{2}$.

PB ■ 85

1 a 8 red cubes, 4 blue cubes
b 6 red cubes, 6 blue cubes
c 9 red cubes, 3 blue cubes
d 12 blue cubes
e 12 blue cubes

2 Child's own investigation.

? Child's own investigation.

PB ■ 86

1 a $\frac{1}{4}$
b $\frac{1}{8}$

c $\frac{2}{8} = \frac{1}{4}$

d 0

e $\frac{1}{2}$

f $\frac{3}{8}$

g $\frac{1}{2}$

h 1

2 a $\frac{3}{4}$ of spinner labelled 4

b $\frac{1}{2}$ of spinner labelled 1

c $\frac{3}{8}$ of spinner labelled 2

d No 5 on spinner

3 Child's own investigation.

? Child's own investigation.

PB ■ 87

1 Child's own statements about the graph.
Possible answers include:
The minimum temperature during the day was 10°C.
The maximum temperature during the day was 22·5°C.
The temperature range was 12·5°C.
The temperature:
increased from 7 am to 10 am;
decreased from 10 am to 1 pm;
increased from 1 pm to 2 pm;
decreased from 3 pm to 6 pm.
It was cooler at lunchtime.
It was warmest at 10 am.
It was coolest at 6 am.

2 Child's own temperature graph.

PB ■ 88

1 a £85

b £19

c £50

d £65

2 a 88 euros

b 40 euros

c 128 euros

3 Child's own answers in pounds sterling and euros.

PB ■ 89

1 a 0–9, 10–19, 20–29, 30–39, 40–49, 50–59, 60–69, 70–79, 80–89, 90–99

b 0–4, 5–9, 10–14, 15–19, 20–24

c 1–50, 51–100, 101–150, 151–200, 201–250, 251–300

d 1–100, 101–200, 201–300, 301–400, 401–500, 501–600, 601–700, 701–800, 801–900, 901–1000

2 Child's own investigation and report. Conclusion likely to vary according to time of year.

PB ■ 90

1 a $\frac{1}{2}$ red, $\frac{1}{2}$ blue

b $\frac{5}{8}$ red, $\frac{3}{8}$ blue

c $\frac{1}{4}$ red, $\frac{3}{4}$ blue

d $\frac{7}{8}$ red, $\frac{1}{8}$ blue

e $\frac{3}{4}$ red, $\frac{1}{4}$ blue

f $\frac{1}{2}$ red, $\frac{1}{2}$ blue

g $\frac{3}{8}$ red, $\frac{5}{8}$ blue

h $\frac{1}{6}$ red, $\frac{5}{6}$ blue

2 netball: $\frac{1}{4}$ of circle, $\frac{1}{4}$ of 48 = 12
rugby: $\frac{1}{16}$ of circle, $\frac{1}{16}$ of 48 = 3
skating: $\frac{1}{16}$ of circle, $\frac{1}{16}$ of 48 = 3
tennis: $\frac{1}{8}$ of circle, $\frac{1}{8}$ of 48 = 6
football: $\frac{1}{4}$ of circle, $\frac{1}{4}$ of 48 = 12
swimming: $\frac{1}{8}$ of circle, $\frac{1}{8}$ of 48 = 6
horse riding: $\frac{1}{8}$ of circle, $\frac{1}{8}$ of 48 = 6

3 Child's own survey results displayed as a pie chart.

? Child's own answer to show that
different sample groups will produce
different survey results.

3 Child's own graph with mode 4 and
range 10.

PB ■ 91

1 a 24, half way: 24
b 78, half way: 97
c 110, half way: 102
d 33, half way: 51·5
e 29, half way: 91·5
f 52, half way: 205

2 a range = 6, mode = 16
b range = 40 cm, mode = 120 cm
c range = 5°C, mode = 20°C
d range = 10, mode = 7

1 a 132 cm
b 15
c $\frac{1}{7}$
d 71 kg
e 106
f 2·5 l
g £5·40
h 600

2 41

3 Child's own answers.

PUPIL BOOK

ACTIVITY SHEETS

AS ■ 1

1 **a** 700
 b 70
 c 7000
 d 7000
 e 700 000
 f 7 000 000

2 **a** 50 413
 b 71 670
 c 827 596
 d 1 230 429

3 **a** 200 000, 40 000, 9000, 700, 10, 8
 b 500 000, 4000, 200, 30, 1
 c 600 000, 20 000, 70, 5

4 3 299 880, 3 299 890, 3 299 910, 3 299 920, 3 299 930, 3 299 940, 3 299 950, 3 299 960, 3 299 970, 3 299 980, 3 299 990, 3 300 010

5 171 tickets have 1 zero
9 tickets have 2 zeros
1 ticket has 3 zeros

? 1 ticket has 3 zeros,
27 tickets have 2 zeros and
243 tickets have 1 zero.

AS ■ 2

1 **a** 7000
 b 62 000
 c 34 000
 d 45 000
 e 65 000

2 **a** 6100 + 3800
 9900
 9928

b 2800 + 3600
6400
6393
c 5900 + 7000
12 900
12 889

3 **a** Any 3 numbers from 54 245 to 54 254.
 b Any 3 numbers from 31 150 to 31 249.
 c Any 3 numbers from 175 500 to 176 499.

4 Child's own answers.

AS ■ 3

1 **a** $^-1$, $^-10$, $^-19$
 b $^-12$, $^-26$, $^-40$
 c $^-4$, $^-17$, $^-30$
 d $^-30$, $^-47$, $^-64$
 e $^-3$, 9, 21
 f $^-7$, 9, 25

2 $^-15$, $^-5$ $^-9$, 1
$^-14$, $^-4$ $^-8$, 2
$^-13$, $^-3$ $^-7$, 3
$^-12$, $^-2$ $^-6$, 4
$^-11$, $^-1$ $^-5$, 5
$^-10$, 0

? If the difference is 11:
$^-15$, $^-4$ $^-10$, 1
$^-14$, $^-3$ $^-9$, 2
$^-13$, $^-2$ $^-8$, 3
$^-12$, $^-1$ $^-7$, 4
$^-11$, 0 $^-6$, 5
If the difference is 12:
$^-15$, $^-3$ $^-10$, 2
$^-14$, $^-2$ $^-9$, 3
$^-13$, $^-1$ $^-8$, 4
$^-12$, 0 $^-7$, 5
$^-11$, 1

1 a 16 20 24 28 32 36
      ↓   ↓   ↓   ↓   ↓   ↓
      6   0   4   8   2   6

b

start

c The pattern produces a
five-pointed star shape.

2 a

start · add 2

start · add 3

start · add 4

start · add 5

start · add 6

start · add 7

start · add 8

start · add 9

b add 2 produces a pentagon.
add 3 produces a 10-pointed
star.
add 4 produces a 5-pointed star.
add 5 produces a straight line.
add 6 produces a 5-pointed star.
add 7 produces a 10-pointed star.

add 8 produces a pentagon.
add 9 produces a decagon.

c The following patterns produce
the same shapes:
add 2 and add 8
add 3 and add 7
add 4 and add 6.

1 Missing numbers from the top
down:
5, 10, 10, 5
6, 15, 20, 15, 6
7, 21, 35, 35, 21, 7
8, 28, 56, 70, 56, 28, 8
9, 36, 84, 126, 126, 84, 36, 9
10, 45, 120, 210, 252, 210, 120,
45, 10
11, 55, 165, 330, 462, 462, 330,
165, 55, 11
12, 66, 220, 495, 792, 924, 792,
495, 220, 66, 12.

2 Odd numbers occur beneath one odd
and one even number.
Even numbers occur beneath two
odd or two even numbers.
The multiples of 3 are arranged in
triangular blocks.
The sloping lines next to the edges of
the triangle are counting numbers.
The next lines are triangular
numbers.

? The first few rows of the triangle are
the same then two copies of
Pascal's triangle begin to appear.

ACTIVITY SHEETS

39

AS ■ 6

1 a Child's drawing

b

Triangle	Value
T(1)	1
T(2)	3
T(3)	6
T(4)	10
T(5)	15
T(6)	21
T(7)	28
T(8)	36
T(9)	45
T(10)	55

2 a Child's drawing

b

Pentagon	Value
P(1)	1
P(2)	5
P(3)	12
P(4)	22
P(5)	35
P(6)	51
P(7)	70
P(8)	92
P(9)	117
P(10)	145

3

	Triangle	Square	Pentagon	Hexagon
1	1	1	1	1
2	3	4	5	6
3	6	9	12	15
4	10	16	22	28
5	15	25	35	45
6	21	36	51	66
7	28	49	70	91
8	36	64	92	120
9	45	81	117	153
10	55	100	145	190

AS ■ 7

1 Child's own answers to show
$E \times E = E$

2 a The product of 2 odd numbers is an **odd** number.
b The product of an odd and an even number is an **even** number.
c Double an odd number plus 1 is an **odd** number.
d 3 times an even number minus 1 is an **odd** number.

3 Child's own answers to show that the statement is only true when the odd number is multiplied by another odd number to form the multiple.

💡 The same conclusion applies if 'add 1 to' is 'subtract 1 from'.

AS ■ 8

1 a 105, 120, 135, 150, 165, 180, 195
b 105, 140, 175
c 165

d No number on the chart is divisible by 3, 5, 7 and 11. The lowest common multiple of 3,5,7 and 11 is 1155.

2

	÷3	÷4	÷5	÷6	÷8	÷9	÷10	÷25
273	✓	✗	✗	✗	✗	✗	✗	✗
300	✓	✓	✓	✓	✗	✗	✓	✓

Possible numbers that could go in box **a** include:
12, 24, 84, 132, 156 …

3 Child's own answers to show a number is divisible by:
3 if the sum of its digits is divisible by 3.
4 if the last 2 digits are divisible by 4.
5 if the last digit is 0 or 5.
6 if it is even and also divisible by 3.
8 if half of it is divisible by 4 or if the last 3 digits are divisible by 8.
9 if the sum of its digits is divisible by 9.
10 if the last digit is 0.

? Child's own answers to show the converse of the tests.
A number is **not** divisible by:
3 if the sum of its digit is not divisible by 3.
4 if the last 2 digits are not divisible by 4.
5 if the last digit is not 0 or 5.
6 if it is not even and also divisible by 3.
8 if half of it is not divisible by 4 or if the last 3 digits are not divisible by 8.
9 if the sum of its digits is not divisible by 9.
10 if the last digit is not 0.

1 Ticks through: 917, 2898, 1106, 3808, 749.
Crosses through: 2898, 1106, 1206, 3808.

1 a

100	225	**400**	**625**	**900**	**1225**	**1600**
difference 125	**175**	**225**	275	325	375	
difference	50	**50**	50	50	50	

b $45^2 = 2025$, $50^2 = 2500$, $55^2 = 3025$

2 Child's working to show:
a $16 \times 15 = 240$
$(15^2 + 15)$
b $21 \times 20 = 420$
$(20^2 + 20)$
c $26 \times 25 = 650$
$(25^2 + 25)$
d $49 \times 50 = 2450$
$(50^2 - 50)$.

3 a 21, 28, 36, 45, 55, 66
b

Triangular number	Triangular number	Sum
1	3	4
3	6	9
6	10	16
10	15	25
15	21	36
21	28	49
28	36	64
36	45	81
45	55	100
55	66	121

c Each pair of triangular numbers has a sum that is a square number.

AS ■ 11

1 1   11
121   121
12 321   1221
1 234 321   12 221
123 454 321   122 221

2 a $3 \times 3 = 9$
$3 \times 33 = 99$
$3 \times 333 = 999$
$3 \times 3333 = 9999$
$3 \times 33\,333 = 99\,999$
$3 \times 333\,333 = 999\,999$
$4 \times 9 = 36$
$44 \times 9 = 396$
$444 \times 9 = 3996$
$4444 \times 9 = 39\,996$
$44\,444 \times 9 = 399\,996$
$444\,444 \times 9 = 3\,999\,996$

b $3 \times 3\,333\,333 = 9\,999\,999$
$3 \times 33\,333\,333 = 99\,999\,999$
$4\,444\,444 \times 9 = 39\,999\,996$
$44\,444\,444 \times 9 = 399\,999\,996$

c Child's description of pattern.

d $3 \times 333\,333\,333 = 999\,999\,999$
$3 \times 3\,333\,333\,333$
   $= 9\,999\,999\,999$
$444\,444\,444 \times 9$
   $= 3\,999\,999\,996$
$4\,444\,444\,444 \times 9$
   $= 39\,999\,999\,996$

Not all sets of numbers produce a clear pattern.

AS ■ 12

1 a $\frac{5}{40} = \frac{1}{8}$
b $\frac{2}{100} = \frac{1}{50}$
c Possible answers include:
$\frac{6}{30} = \frac{1}{5}, \frac{12}{30} = \frac{2}{5}, \frac{18}{30} = \frac{3}{5}, \frac{24}{30} = \frac{4}{5}.$
d Possible answers include:
$\frac{9}{180} = \frac{1}{20}, \frac{9}{90} = \frac{2}{20}, \frac{9}{60} = \frac{3}{20},$

$\frac{9}{45} = \frac{4}{20}, \frac{9}{36} = \frac{5}{20}, \frac{9}{18} = \frac{10}{20},$
$\frac{9}{15} = \frac{12}{20}, \frac{9}{12} = \frac{15}{20}, \frac{9}{10} = \frac{18}{20}.$
e $\frac{8}{40} = \frac{1}{5}$

f Possible answers include:
$\frac{80}{100} = \frac{4}{5}, \frac{50}{100} = \frac{4}{8}, \frac{40}{100} = \frac{4}{10},$
$\frac{25}{100} = \frac{4}{16}, \frac{20}{100} = \frac{4}{20}, \frac{16}{100} = \frac{4}{25}$
$\frac{10}{100} = \frac{4}{40}.$

2 a $\frac{40}{7} = 5\frac{5}{7}$
b $\frac{20}{3} = 6\frac{2}{3}$
c $\frac{50}{6} = 8\frac{1}{3}$
d $\frac{25}{10} = 2\frac{1}{2}$
e $\frac{60}{8} = 7\frac{1}{2}$
f Possible answers include:
$\frac{14}{100} = 1\frac{2}{5}, \frac{24}{10} = 2\frac{2}{5}, \frac{34}{10} = 3\frac{2}{5} \dots$

AS ■ 14

1 a $2\frac{1}{2} = \frac{5}{2}$
b $6\frac{1}{2} = \frac{13}{2}$
c $3\frac{1}{2} = \frac{7}{2}$
d $1\frac{1}{4} = \frac{5}{4}$
e $4\frac{3}{4} = \frac{19}{4}$
f $3\frac{1}{8} = \frac{25}{8}$
g $7\frac{1}{4} = \frac{29}{4}$ or $7\frac{1}{2} = \frac{30}{4}$
h $5\frac{1}{2} = \frac{44}{8}$
i $6\frac{2}{8} = \frac{50}{8}$ or $6\frac{1}{4} = \frac{50}{8}$

2 a $\frac{3}{5}$ of £1 = **60** p
b $\frac{5}{8}$ of 48 m = **30** m
c $\frac{7}{8}$ of 112 = 98
d $\frac{4}{7}$ of 490 = 280
e $\frac{7}{10}$ of 200 = 140
f Possible answers include:
$\frac{5}{60}$ of 1 hr = **5** min,
$\frac{5}{10}$ of 1 hr = **30** min,
$\frac{5}{15}$ of 1 hr = **20** min,
$\frac{5}{20}$ of 1 hr = **15** min,
$\frac{5}{25}$ of 1 hr = **12** min,
$\frac{5}{30}$ of 1 hr = **10** min,
$\frac{5}{50}$ of 1 hr = **6** min.

AS ■ 15

1 a Child's shading to show total of 9 blue and 3 yellow squares.

b Child's shading to show 4 yellow squares.

2 Child's own pattern covering 96 squares of the grid.

AS ■ 16

1 7·663, 7·636, 7·366, 6·763, 6·736, 6·673, 6·637, 6·376, 6·367, 3·766, 3·676, 3·667
3·667 lies between 3·66 and 3·67
Possible answers include: 3·661, 3·662, 3·663, 3·664, 3·665, 3·666, 3·667, 3·668, 3·669.

AS ■ 20

1 a $30\% = \frac{3}{10}$

b $80\% = \frac{4}{5}$

c $75\% = \frac{3}{4}$

d $40\% = \frac{2}{5}$

e $25\% = \frac{1}{4}$

f $10\% = \frac{1}{10}$

g Possible answers include:
$75\% = \frac{3}{4}$, $60\% = \frac{3}{5}$, $50\% = \frac{3}{6}$,
$25\% = \frac{3}{12}$, $20\% = \frac{3}{15}$, $15\% = \frac{3}{20}$,
$12\% = \frac{3}{25}$, $10\% = \frac{3}{30}$, $6\% = \frac{3}{50}$,
$5\% = \frac{3}{60}$, $4\% = \frac{3}{75}$, $3\% = \frac{3}{100}$,
$2\% = \frac{3}{120}$, $1\% = \frac{3}{300}$.

h Possible answers include:
$5\% = \frac{1}{20}$, $10\% = \frac{2}{20}$, $15\% = \frac{3}{20}$,
$20\% = \frac{4}{20}$, $25\% = \frac{5}{20}$, $30\% = \frac{6}{20}$,
$35\% = \frac{7}{20}$, $40\% = \frac{8}{20}$, $45\% = \frac{9}{20}$,
$50\% = \frac{10}{20}$, $55\% = \frac{11}{20}$, $60\% = \frac{12}{20}$,
$65\% = \frac{13}{20}$, $70\% = \frac{14}{20}$, $75\% = \frac{15}{20}$,
$80\% = \frac{16}{20}$, $85\% = \frac{17}{20}$, $90\% = \frac{18}{20}$,
$95\% = \frac{19}{20}$.

i Child's own answer.

2 a 15% of £1 = **15**p

b 36% of 1 km = **360** m

c 73% of 1 kg = **730** g

d **25**% of 84 = 21

e 20% of **200** = 40

f Child's own answer.

AS ■ 21

1

68	22	46	23	14	2
51	36	62	57	39	13
27	48	82	73	37	17

2 0·9 0·1, 1·1 8·9, 8·2 1·8, 3·8 6·2, 4·8 5·2, 7·4 2·6, 0·6 0·4

3 250, 650, 200, 150, 400, 905

4 Child's own answers.
Start and finish numbers are the same because for each operation on the number there was an inverse operation.

AS ■ 22

1 a 5873

b 9857

c 3984

d 3984

e 3984

f 9857

2

Additions
$2406 + 2119 = 4525$
$6421 + 1536 = 7957$
$1536 + 6421 = 7957$
$2119 + 1536 = 3655$
$1536 + 2119 = 3655$

Subtractions
$4525 - 2119 = 2406$
$7957 - 6421 = 1536$
$7957 - 1536 = 6421$
$3655 - 2119 = 1536$
$3655 - 1536 = 2119$

3 *a* 835
   b 5087
   c 3300
   d 2109

AS ■ 23

1 *a* 3, 4
   b 4, 7, 0
   c 8, 8, 3, 9

2 *a* 6 boxes
   b 999·33 kg
   c 362·4 kg

3 6789, 6798, 6879, 6897, 6978, 6987,
7689, 7698, 7869, 7896, 7968, 7986,
8679, 8697, 8769, 8796, 8967, 8976,
9678, 9687, 9768, 9786, 9867, 9876

Answer is between	
13 000 and 14 000	Any 6000 number added to any 6000 number
14 000 and 15 000	Any 6000 number added to any 7000 number
15 000 and 16 000	Any 6000 number added to any 8000 number Any 7000 number added to any 7000 number
16 000 and 17 000	Any 6000 number added to any 9000 number Any 7000 number added to any 8000 number
17 000 and 18 000	Any 7000 number added to any 9000 number Any 8000 number added to any 8000 number
18 000 and 19 000	Any 8000 number added to any 9000 number
19 000 and 20 000	Any 9000 number added to any 9000 number

AS ■ 24

1 **a** 719
   b 2227
   c 5098
   d 3856
   e 6339
   f 6496
   The 3-letter word is: COT.

2 Child's own answers to show the 'ending' is always zero.
Unless the starting number is a palindrome, the pattern will reach a number with repeating digits of the $9\times$ table and then 909, which finally results in zero.

AS ■ 25

1 **a** 8681 or 9301
   b 2502
   c 1004 or 834

2 **a** 1115, 1115, 1110
   b 6660, 6660, 6665

AS ■ 26

1 **a** 52, 26
   b 940, 47
   c 15, 45

2

Year	Amount	10%	New Amount
1999	£1000	£100	£1100
2000	£1100	**£110**	**£1210**
2001	**£1210**	**£121**	**£1331**
2002	**£1331**	**£133·10**	**£1464·10**
2003	**£1464·10**	**£146·41**	**£1610·51**
	Total added:	**£610·51**	

3 **a** The £98 000 house coloured yellow.
   b The £275 000 house coloured red.
   c The £130 000 house coloured blue.

AS ■ 27

1

	4 traders	5 traders	6 traders	7 traders
67 kg of grain	$16\frac{3}{4}$ kg	$13\frac{2}{5}$ kg	**$11\frac{1}{6}$ kg**	**$9\frac{4}{7}$ kg**
37 kg of grain	$9\frac{1}{4}$ kg	**$7\frac{2}{5}$ kg**	**$6\frac{1}{6}$ kg**	**$5\frac{2}{7}$ kg**
49 kg of grain	**$12\frac{1}{4}$ kg**	**$9\frac{4}{5}$ kg**	**$8\frac{1}{6}$ kg**	**7 kg**
90 kg of grain	**$22\frac{1}{2}$ kg**	**18 kg**	**15 kg**	**$12\frac{6}{7}$ kg**

2 $101 \div 8 = 12\frac{5}{8}$, $109 \div 8 = 13\frac{5}{8}$,
   $117 \div 8 = 14\frac{5}{8}$,
   $125 \div 8 = 15\frac{5}{8}$, $133 \div 8 = 16\frac{5}{8}$,
   $141 \div 8 = 17\frac{5}{8}$, $149 \div 8 = 18\frac{5}{8}$

? Add 2 to answers from question 2:
   $103 \div 8 = 12\frac{7}{8}$, $111 \div 8 = 13\frac{7}{8}$,
   $119 \div 8 = 14\frac{7}{8}$,
   $127 \div 8 = 15\frac{7}{8}$, $135 \div 8 = 16\frac{7}{8}$,
   $143 \div 8 = 17\frac{7}{8}$.

AS ■ 28

1 **a** 9
   b 8
   c 8
   d 8
   e 42
   f Three quarters

2

	divided by								
	2	3	4	5	6	7	8	9	10
36	18	12	9		6			4	
40	20		10	8			5		4
54	27	18			9			6	
63		21				9		7	
72	36	24	18		12		9	8	
83									

ACTIVITY SHEETS

AS ■ 29

1 a 94
  b 79
  c 89
  d 2240
  e 2900
  f Two

2 a 36
  b 49
  c 64
  d 81
  e 100

3 a 400
  b 900
  c 1600
  d 2500
  e 3600
  f 4900
  g 6400
  h 8100

4 $1^2 = 1$, $11^2 = 121$, $111^2 = 12321$,
  $1111^2 = 1234321$,
  $11\,111^2 = 123454321$
  To make the next square in the
  pattern, repeat the highest number in
  the middle then insert the next
  higher number between the two.

? $1^2 = 1$, $101^2 = 10201$,
  $1001^2 = 1002001$,
  $10001^2 = 100020001$

AS ■ 30

1 a 132
  b 255, 5, 17, 3, 85, 255

2 a $3 \times 160 = 480$
  b $24 \times 7 \times 2 = 168 \times 2 = 336$
  c $28 \times 7 \times 3 = 196 \times 3 = 588$
  d $11 \times 2 \times 23 = 11 \times 46 = 506$

3 a $7 \times 5 \times 9 \times 2 = 10 \times 9 \times 7$
     $= 90 \times 7 = 630$
  b $2 \times 7 \times 5 \times 5 = 10 \times 7 \times 5$
     $= 70 \times 5 = 350$
  c Possible answers include:
     $5 \times 3 \times 48 \times 2 = 10 \times 48 \times 3$
        $= 480 \times 3$
        $= 1440,$
     $5 \times 3 \times 24 \times 4 = 20 \times 24 \times 3$
        $= 480 \times 3$
        $= 1440.$
  d Possible answers include:
     $9 \times 5 \times 12 \times 4 = 20 \times 108$
        $= 2160,$
     $9 \times 5 \times 6 \times 8 = 30 \times 9 \times 8$
        $= 270 \times 8$
        $= 2160,$
     $9 \times 5 \times 24 \times 2 = 10 \times 9 \times 24$
        $= 90 \times 24$
        $= 2160.$

AS ■ 31

1 Possible answers include:
  $51 \times 14 = 714$, $51 \times 17 = 867$,
  $51 \times 19 = 969$, $51 \times 23 = 1173$,
  $51 \times 49 = 2499,$

  $49 \times 14 = 686$, $49 \times 17 = 833$,
  $49 \times 19 = 931$, $49 \times 23 = 1127$,
  $49 \times 51 = 2499,$

  $23 \times 14 = 322$, $23 \times 17 = 391$,
  $23 \times 19 = 437$, $23 \times 49 = 1127$,
  $23 \times 51 = 1173,$

  $19 \times 14 = 266$, $19 \times 17 = 323$,
  $19 \times 23 = 437$, $19 \times 49 = 931$,
  $19 \times 51 = 969,$

  $17 \times 14 = 238$, $17 \times 19 = 323$,
  $17 \times 23 = 391$, $17 \times 49 = 833$,
  $17 \times 51 = 867,$

  $14 \times 17 = 238$, $14 \times 19 = 266$,
  $14 \times 23 = 322$, $14 \times 49 = 686$,
  $14 \times 51 = 714.$

2

Item	Cost for 1	Cost for 50	Cost for 49	Cost for 51
Crisps	32p	£16	**£15·68**	**£16·32**
Sports drink	56p	£28	**£27·44**	**£28·56**
Blank CD	72p	**£36**	£35·28	£36·72
Magazine	95p	**£47·50**	**£46·55**	**£48·45**
Tennis ball	99p	**£49·50**	**£48·51**	**£50·49**

3 Child's own answers to show that the half way number is equal to the original number multiplied by 40. A number multiplied by 39 is equal to (40 × the number) − (1 × the number). A number multiplied by 41 is equal to (40 × the number) + (1 × the number).

(?) The halfway number is equal to the original number multiplied by 50. A number multiplied by 49 is equal to (50 × the number) − (1 × the number). A number multiplied by 51 is equal to (50 × the number) + (1 × the number).

AS ■ 32

1 *a* 14
  b 751
  c 290
  d 6·3
  e 0·09
  f 0·047

2 *a* 76, 7·6, 0·76
  b 8, 0·8, 0·08
  c 12·5, 1·25, 0·125

3 Child's own answers to show that Lia's statement is true.

(?) The two answers differ by 0·01.

AS ■ 33

1

Multiplication	Approximate answer	Exact answer
4·2 × 5	20	21
5·3 × 4	20	21·2
6·6 × 6	42	39·6
7·8 × 8	64	62·4

Multiplication	Approximate answer	Exact answer
11·7 × 9	108	105·3
13·2 × 7	91	92·4
15·8 × 6	96	94·8
17·3 × 8	136	138·4

2 *a* ✓
  b ✗ 5·72 × 6 = 34·32
  c ✗ 7·93 × 5 = 39·65
  d ✓
  e ✓
  f ✗ 8·74 × 9 = 78·66

3 12 of the following, written in order of increasing size:
4·56 × 7 = 31·92, 4·65 × 7 = 32·55,
4·57 × 6 = 27·42, 4·75 × 6 = 28·5,
4·67 × 5 = 23·35, 4·76 × 5 = 23·8
5·46 × 7 = 38·22, 5·64 × 7 = 39·48,
5·47 × 6 = 32·82, 5·74 × 6 = 34·44,
5·67 × 4 = 22·68, 5·76 × 4 = 23·04,
6·45 × 7 = 45·15, 6·54 × 7 = 45·78,
6·47 × 5 = 32·35, 6·74 × 5 = 33·7,
6·57 × 4 = 26·28, 6·75 × 4 = 27,
7·45 × 6 = 44·7, 7·54 × 6 = 45·24,
7·46 × 5 = 37·3, 7·64 × 5 = 38·2,
7·56 × 4 = 30·24, 7·65 × 4 = 30·6.

(?) The answers would be the same with the digits moved one place to the left:
$45 \cdot 6 \times 7 = 319 \cdot 2$,
$46 \cdot 5 \times 7 = 325 \cdot 5$,
$45 \cdot 7 \times 6 = 274 \cdot 2$,
$47 \cdot 5 \times 6 = 285 \ldots$

AS ■ 34

1 *a* 19 764
 b 31 616
 c 45 668

2 *a* 6
 b 9
 c 9
 d 3

3 924×63, 882×66, 756×77, 693×84, 594×98, 588×99

(?) There are 3 possible answers:
9702×6, 8316×7, 6468×9.

AS ■ 35

1

Division	Approximate answer	Exact answer as a mixed number	Multiplication check
$188 \div 6$	30	$31\frac{2}{6}$ or $31\frac{1}{3}$	$31 \times 6 = 186$
$254 \div 9$	30	$28\frac{2}{9}$	$28 \times 9 = 252$
$249 \div 6$	40	$41\frac{3}{6}$ or $41\frac{1}{2}$	$41 \times 6 = 246$
$342 \div 7$	50	$48\frac{6}{7}$	$48 \times 7 = 336$
$295 \div 8$	40	$36\frac{7}{8}$	$36 \times 8 = 288$
$443 \div 7$	60	$63\frac{2}{7}$	$63 \times 7 = 441$

2 $369 \div 9$ gives the closest answer to 40
$369 \div 9 = 41$.

AS ■ 36

1 *a* 77
 b 32 miles
 c 21
 d 18
 e 26 m
 f 61 mph
 g 25
 h 34
 i 74
 j £58
The 3-letter word is: TOY.

AS ■ 37

1 *a* $493782 + 810098 = 130\mathbf{3}880$
 b $\mathbf{651} \times 297 = 19334\mathbf{7}$
 c $117\mathbf{166} - 30491 = 866\mathbf{75}$
 d $224466 \div 358 = 627$

2 *a* $4 + 8 + 16 + 32 + 64 + 128 = 252$
 b $256 + 128 + 64 + 32 + 16 + 8 = 504$

3 *a* $332 + 217 + 101 = 650$
 $284 + 204 + 162 = 650$
 $312 + 255 + 83 = 650$

AS ■ 38

1

Miles	Kilometres
0	0
5	8
10	16
15	24
20	32
25	40
30	48

2 A straight line joining (0, 0) to (40, 64) drawn on the graph.

3 a 25 miles
  b 64 km
  c 40 miles
  d 7·5 miles
  e 28 km
  f 36 km

4 a 3890 m = 3·89 km ≈ 4 km
    ≈ 2·5 miles
  b 11 700 m = 11·7 km ≈ 12 km
    ≈ 7·5 miles

5 a 80 km, 33 km
  b Brough

AS ■ 39

1 a 50 g
  b 2 oz
  c 200 g
  d 13 oz
  e 250 g
  f 8 oz
  g 450 g
  h 15 oz

2 a 4 oz > 100 g
  b 13 oz > 350 g
  c 6 oz < 175 g
  d 14 oz < 400 g

3

	1 oz	2 oz	4 oz	8 oz	16 oz	32 oz	64 oz	Check
28 oz			✓	✓	✓			4 + 8 + 16 = 28
19 oz	✓	✓			✓			1 + 2 + 16 = 19
41 oz	✓			✓		✓		1 + 8 + 32 = 41
53 oz	✓		✓		✓	✓		1 + 4 + 16 + 32 = 53
4 lb							✓	64 oz = 4 lb

4 The referee must balance the balls 4
times to find the odd one out.
Balance 8 balls against the other 8.
Take the lighter 8 and balance 4
against 4. Take the lighter set and

balance 2 against 2. Finally balance
the lighter 2 against each other.

AS ■ 40

50 l

AS ■ 41

1 a

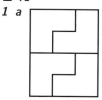

P = 14 cm

  b

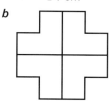

P = 16 cm

  c

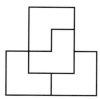

P = 16 cm

d

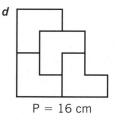

P = 16 cm

e

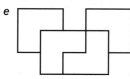

P = 18 cm

f

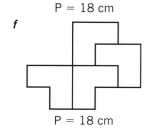

P = 18 cm

2 Child's own answers with P = 20 cm.
Possible answers include:

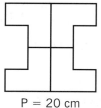

P = 20 cm

❓ Child's own answers.

AS ■ 43
Child's own answers.

AS ■ 44
1 a

n	1	2	3	4	5	6	7	8
n + 2	3	4	5	6	7	8	9	10

b Child's completed pattern.
c The lines form an 18-sided polygon inside the circle.

2 a

n	1	2	3	4	5	6	7	8
n + 5	6	7	8	9	10	11	12	13

Child's completed pattern.
The lines form an 18-pointed star and a smaller 18-sided polygon inside the circle.

b

n	1	2	3	4	5	6	7	8
n + 8	9	10	11	12	13	14	15	16

Child's completed pattern.
The lines form 2 9-pointed stars, each with a 9-sided polygon inside.
Together they make an 18-pointed star with an 18-sided polygon inside.

AS ■ 45
1 a A = rectangle
B = square
C = trapezium
D = parallelogram
E = rhombus
F = kite
G = trapezium
b Child's drawn in diagonals.
c

Property of diagonal lines	Quadrilateral						
	A	B	C	D	E	F	G
are the same length	✓	✓	✗	✗	✗	✗	✓
bisect each other	✓	✓	✗	✓	✓	✗	✗
intersect at right angles	✗	✓	✗	✗	✓	✓	✗

ACTIVITY SHEETS

d The diagonals of the square, rhombus and kite intersect at right angles.

e Both diagonals of the square and rhombus, and the longer of those of the kite should be coloured red.

f Square, rhombus, kite.

2 Child's statement to indicate that the diagonals of any square, rectangle, rhombus or parallelogram bisect one another.

AS ■ 46

1 Child's coloured paths.

2 The checkpoints should be labelled from the top down:

start
1, 1
1, 2, 1
1, 3, 3, 1
1, 4, 6, 4, 1
1, 5, 10, 10, 5, 1

3 20

AS ■ 47

1

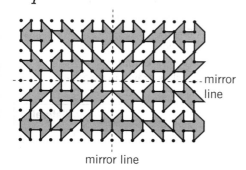

mirror line

mirror line

2

mirror line

mirror line

AS ■ 48

1 *a* Child's translations of each shape.

   b A = trapezium,
      B = triangle,
      C = quadrilateral

2 *a* (5, 3), (8, 5), (7, 7)

   b Shape C has been translated **3** units to the **left** and **4** units **down** to make shape D.

AS ■ 49

1 *a* (⁻1, 1), (2, 1), (2, ⁻1), (⁻1, ⁻1)
   b (0, 3), (2, 0), (0, ⁻3), (⁻2, 0)
   c (⁻1, 3), (⁻1, ⁻2), (⁻3, ⁻1), (⁻3, 1)

2 *a* Points plotted on AS50
   b kite
   c (⁻1, ⁻1)

3 *a* Points plotted on AS50
   b trapezium (⁻2, 3), (⁻4, 5), (⁻4, ⁻3), (⁻2, ⁻1)

4 *a* R(3, ⁻1), S(3, 3) or R(⁻5, ⁻1), S(⁻5, 3)
   b R(⁻5, ⁻1), S(⁻5, 3) or R(3, ⁻1), S(3, 3)

1 a

Angle	A	B	C	D	E	F	G	H
Degrees	72°	72°	72°	72°	72°	54°	54°	72°

b A + B + C + D + E = 360°
F + G + H = 180°

2 a

Angle	J	K	L	M	N	P	Q
Degrees	60°	120°	30°	30°	90°	30°	60°

b P + Q = 90°
c J + K = 180°

3 a

Angle	R	S	T	U	V	W	X
Degrees	135°	22·5°	22·5°	67·5°	45°	67·5°	45°

b R + S + T = 180° (181° if
measured to nearest degree)
S + T + U = 180° (181° if
measured to nearest degree)

c The two angles adjacent to V, the
one adjacent to W, and X are the
same size as angle V.

4 Children write about what they have
discovered. This may include
statements about: the sum of angles
round a point, on a straight line and
in a triangle; each angle of a regular
pentagon (108°), hexagon (120°)
and octagon (135°).

1 a (3, 2), (−2, 3), (−3, −2), (2, −3)
b (4, 2), (−2, 4), (−4, −2), (2, −4)
c (3, 4), (−4, 3), (−3, −4), (4, −3)

3 a
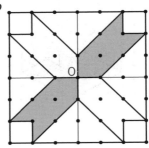

b
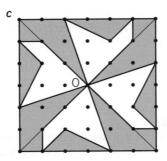

c
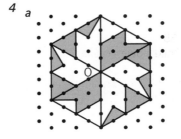

4 a

b

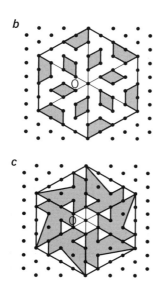

c

1

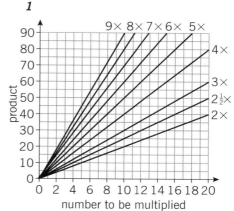

number to be multiplied

2 a 78
b 72
c 57
d 85

3 a 15
b $22\frac{1}{2}$
c 40

4 a 24·5
b 35
c 55·8

AS ■ 53

1 Ticks beside:
On a 1–6 dice you will roll a number less than 5. You will go to the shop this week. It will snow next winter.

2 Child's own answers.

AS ■ 54

2 Arrows drawn on probability line at $\frac{1}{4}$ of length for box and triangle, and at $\frac{1}{2}$ for the circle.

AS ■ 55

1 Child's own answers.

2 Child's own answers based on results in question 1.

3 Probability of 1 is $\frac{2}{6}$ or $\frac{1}{3}$,
probability of 2 is $\frac{2}{6}$ or $\frac{1}{3}$,
probability of 3 is $\frac{1}{6}$,
probability of 4 is $\frac{1}{6}$.

AS ■ 57

1

Ball numbers	Frequency
1–10	749
11–20	703
21–30	759
31–40	780
41–50	758

2 Children's own answers reflecting that the numbers 41–50 occurred most frequently and 11–20 least frequently but there is no very marked differences between the frequencies.

ACTIVITY SHEETS

The bar chart does not show which individual numbers occurred the most and least frequently.

AS ■ 58

1 a 3 sectors coloured red, 6 sectors coloured blue
b 9 sectors coloured red, 2 sectors coloured blue
c 9 sectors coloured red, 1 sector coloured blue

2 Pie chart completed and coloured with 1 sector representing 5 children.

3 Child's own answers.

AS ■ 59

1 a

	Range	Mode
Round 1 Heat 1	0·33 sec	10·03 sec
Round 1 Heat 2	0·18 sec	10·27 sec
Round 1 Heat 3	0·28 sec	10·32 sec

b 9·85 − 10·34
Range = 0·49 seconds

2 a

Time	Frequency
9·85–9·89 secs	1
9·90–9·94 secs	1
9·95–9·99 secs	1
10·00–10·04 secs	6
10·05–10·09 secs	3
10·10–10·14 secs	5
10·15–10·19 secs	5
10·20–10·24 secs	3
10·25–10·29 secs	12
10·30–10·34 secs	11

b

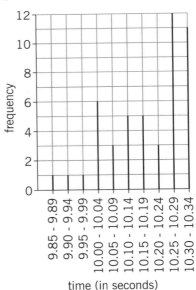

time (in seconds)